EYES OF THE STORM

BY JEFF SMITH

WITH COLOUR BY STEVE HAMAKER

HarperCollins *Children's Books*

This book is for my parents,
Barbara Goodsell and William Earl Smith

This colour edition first published in hardback in the USA by Graphix, an imprint of Scholastic Inc., 2006

First published in Great Britain by HarperCollins *Children's Books* 2007
HarperCollins *Children's Books* is a division of HarperCollins*Publishers* Ltd
77-85 Fulham Palace Road, Hammersmith, London W6 8JB

The HarperCollins *Children's Books* website address is
www.harpercollinschildrensbooks.co.uk

1

Acknowledgements

Harvestar Family Crest designed by Charles Vess
Map of the Valley by Mark Crilley

ISBN-13 978-0-00-724478-2
ISBN-10 0-00-724478-9

Printed and bound by MKT PRINT in Slovenia

CONTENTS

WATERFALL
DRAGON'S STAIR
DEREN GARD
HOT SPRINGS
GRAN'MA BEN'S FARM
OLD MAN'S CAVE
BARRELHAVEN TAVERN
THE FAIRGROUNDS
STONY
N
E
W
S
The Valley

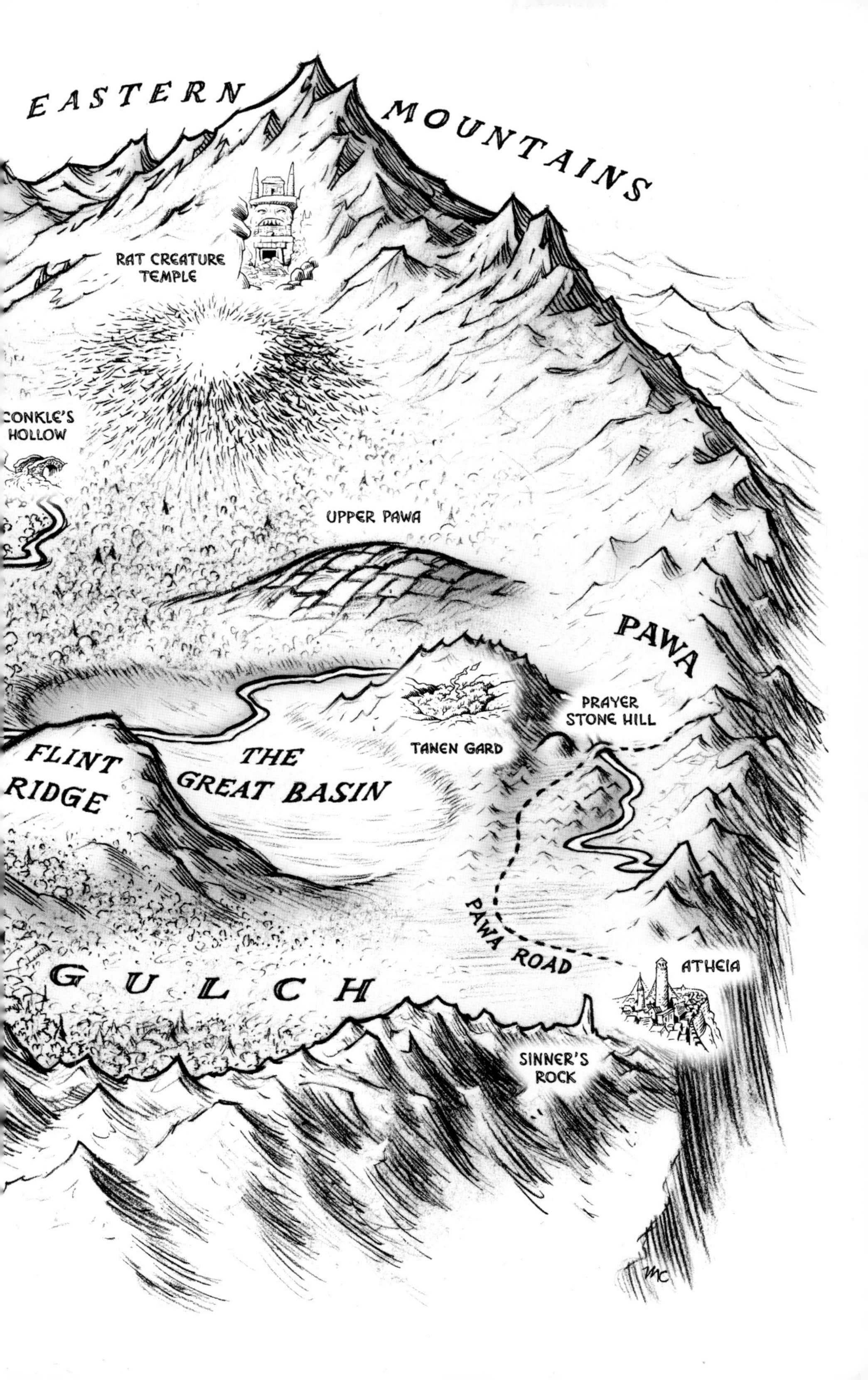
EASTERN MOUNTAINS
RAT CREATURE TEMPLE
CONKLE'S HOLLOW
UPPER PAWA
PAWA
PRAYER STONE HILL
TANEN GARD
FLINT RIDGE
THE GREAT BASIN
PAWA ROAD
ATHEIA
GULCH
SINNER'S ROCK
MC

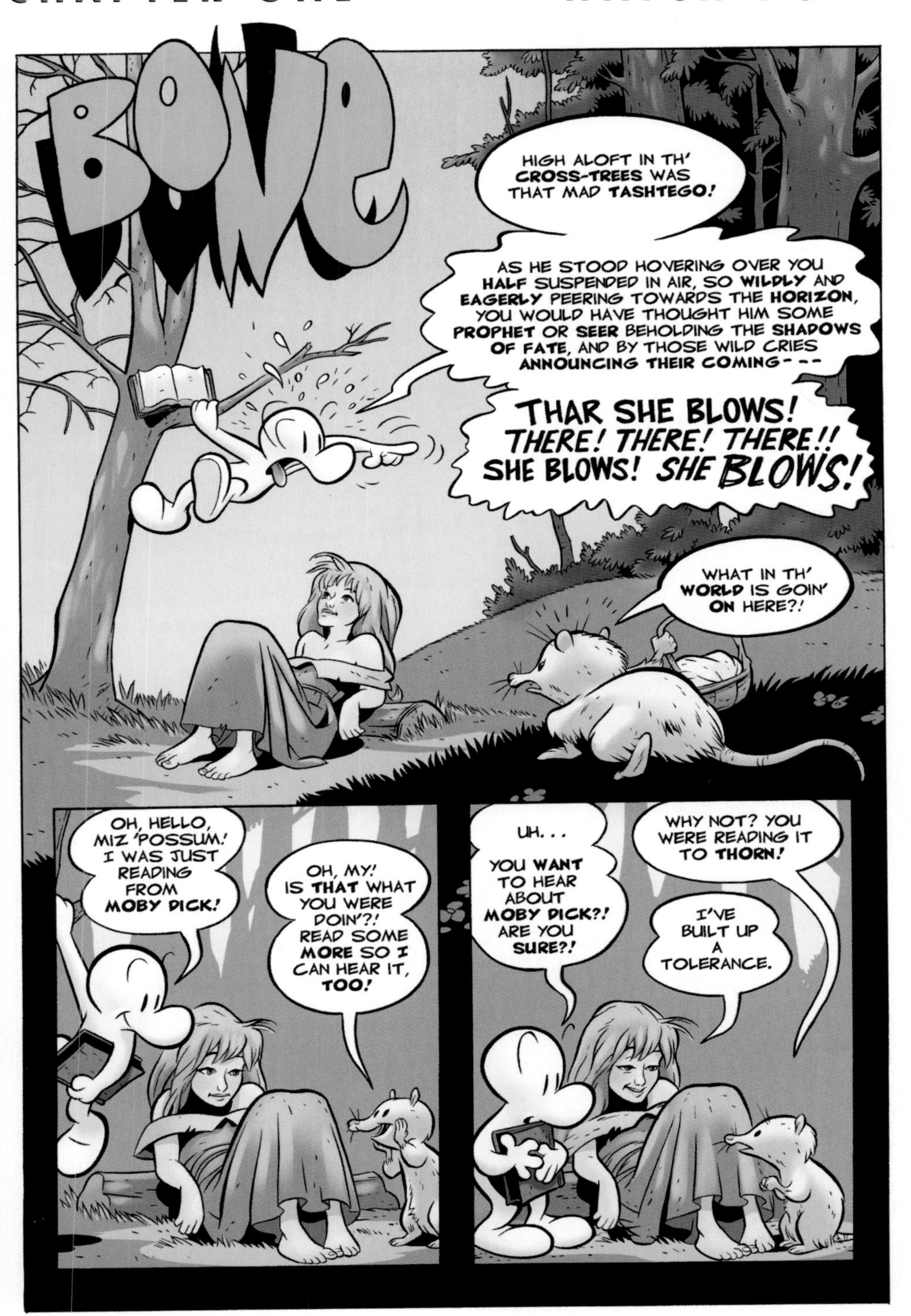
BONE
HIGH ALOFT IN TH' CROSS-TREES WAS THAT MAD TASHTEGO!
AS HE STOOD HOVERING OVER YOU HALF SUSPENDED IN AIR, SO WILDLY AND EAGERLY PEERING TOWARDS THE HORIZON, YOU WOULD HAVE THOUGHT HIM SOME PROPHET OR SEER BEHOLDING THE SHADOWS OF FATE, AND BY THOSE WILD CRIES ANNOUNCING THEIR COMING---
THAR SHE BLOWS! THERE! THERE! THERE!! SHE BLOWS! SHE BLOWS!
WHAT IN TH' WORLD IS GOIN' ON HERE?!
OH, HELLO, MIZ 'POSSUM! I WAS JUST READING FROM MOBY DICK!
OH, MY! IS THAT WHAT YOU WERE DOIN'?! READ SOME MORE SO I CAN HEAR IT, TOO!
UH...
YOU WANT TO HEAR ABOUT MOBY DICK?! ARE YOU SURE?!
WHY NOT? YOU WERE READING IT TO THORN!
I'VE BUILT UP A TOLERANCE.

MAYBE I'LL READ IT LATER. SO, WHAT BRINGS YOU BY, MIZ 'POSSUM?
OH, YOU KNOW **ME**, BONE! I'M ALWAYS **CHECKIN' UP** ON THINGS - - MAKIN' SURE EVERYBODY'S **OKAY**!

I SEE YOU BEEN WORKIN' ON TH' **FARMHOUSE**! HOW'S THAT GOIN'?

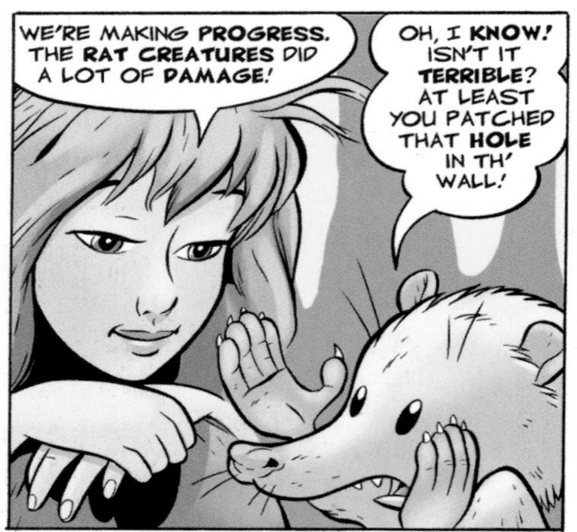
WE'RE MAKING **PROGRESS**. THE **RAT CREATURES** DID A LOT OF **DAMAGE**!
OH, I **KNOW**! ISN'T IT **TERRIBLE**? AT LEAST YOU PATCHED THAT **HOLE** IN TH' WALL!

AN' NOT A **MOMENT** TOO SOON! YOU NEVER KNOW WHEN THOSE **HOOLIGANS** MIGHT COME BACK!

GRAN'MA THINKS TH' RAT CREATURES WILL STAY AWAY FOR A WHILE.
WELL, YOU'RE PROBABLY ALL RIGHT DURIN' TH' **DAYTIME**, BUT DON'T TAKE CHANCES AT **NIGHT**! YOU'RE NOT STILL SLEEPIN' **OUTSIDE**, ARE YOU?

NO, MA'AM! WE'RE ALL SLEEPIN' INDOORS! IN TH' **BIG ROOM** DOWNSTAIRS!
AS SOON AS LUCIUS AND SMILEY FINISH THE **ROOF**, WE'LL MOVE INTO THE BEDROOMS **UPSTAIRS**.
THAT'S GOOD, ANYWAY. . .

AN' WHAT ABOUT THAT GREEDY COUSIN OF YOURS? PHONEY BONE? I HEAR HE CAUSED QUITE A RUCKUS AT THAT COW RACE!
GRAN'MA'S MAKIN' HIM SHOVEL OUT TH' BARN. . .
WITH A SPOON!

SERVES HIM RIGHT! WELL, I'D LOVE TO STAY AN' GOSSIP ALL DAY, BUT I LEFT TH' KIDS WITH MIZ HEDGEHOG, AN' I PROMISED I WOULDN'T BE GONE LONG.
HERE, BONE! I BROUGHT THIS FOR YOU!

SILLY ME! I ALMOST FORGOT TO ASK . . . TH' BOYS WANTED ME TO FIND OUT HOW YOUR GRANDMOTHER DID IN TH' RACE, DEAR!
SHE WON!

THAT'S WONDERFUL! OKAY! NOW I REALLY MUST BE LEAVING! IF YOU NEED ANYTHING AT ALL, YOU JUST HOLLER, YOU HEAR?

OH! AND THAT STUFF IN TH' PAN? IF YOU HAVE ANY LEAKS IN THAT NEW ROOF OF YOURS - - - -

- - JUST SMEAR THAT GOO OVER IT! SEALS UP ANYTHING! GUARANTEED!
THANKS FOR DROPPING BY, MIZ 'POSSUM.

SHE'S RIGHT ABOUT NOT TAKING CHANCES AFTER DARK. WE SHOULD START BACK.
OKAY.

WHOSE TURN IS IT TO STAY UP ON WATCH DUTY?
MINE.

I'LL STAY UP WITH YA IF YA WANT.
YOU SHOULD GET SOME SLEEP. I DON'T MIND STAYING UP BY MYSELF.

BESIDES, AS LONG AS I'M AWAKE, I CAN'T HAVE ANY MORE OF THOSE DREAMS!
DID YOU HAVE ANOTHER WEIRD DREAM?

I HAVEN'T HAD ONE FOR A FEW DAYS NOW, BUT I KEEP WAITING. I'M ALMOST AFRAID TO GO TO SLEEP AT NIGHT!

Y'KNOW, I CAN'T THINK OF A SINGLE DREAM I'VE HAD SINCE I CAME TO THIS VALLEY.
NOT ONE? DO YOU USUALLY REMEMBER YOUR DREAMS?

WATCH DUTY

I ALWAYS REMEMBER MY DREAMS!
HMM. WELL, THINGS ARE A LOT DIFFERENT HERE THAN THEY ARE IN BONEVILLE! MAYBE YOU JUST NEED SOME TIME TO ADJUST.

ME?! BOY! I'LL TELL YA WHO NEEDS TO DO A LITTLE ADJUSTING! PHONEY BONE!
WHY? HE'S FINALLY STARTING TO FIT IN AROUND HERE! AT LEAST HE'S STOPPED COMPLAINING ABOUT HIS CHORES!

THAT JUST MEANS HE'S UP TO SOMETHIN'! HE NEVER LEARNS!
YOU'RE TOO HARD ON HIM. BACK WHERE YOU'RE FROM, PHONEY WAS WEALTHY! IMAGINE WHAT IT MUST BE LIKE TO FIND YOURSELF IN A PLACE WHERE EVERYTHING YOU VALUE IS COMPLETELY WORTHLESS!

YEAH. PHONEY SURE LOVED HIS MONEY! WHAT I WOULDN'T HAVE GIVEN TO SEE HIS FACE WHEN HE FOUND OUT YOU DON'T USE MONEY HERE!

HEH. HIS JAW MUST'VE HIT TH' FLOOR WHEN HE FIGURED OUT YOUR WHOLE ECONOMY IS BASED ON POULTRY PRODUCTS!
HE SEEMS TO HAVE ADJUSTED WELL.

YOU'RE RIGHT! A LITTLE HONEST WORK, AND CLEAN, SIMPLE LIVING WILL DO HIM GOOD!
HI, GUYS!

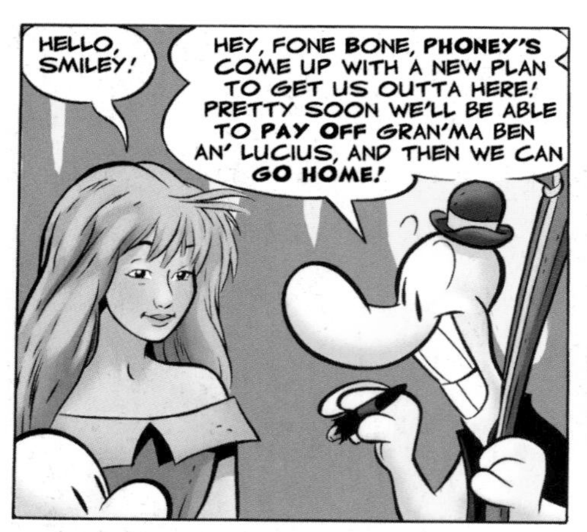
HELLO, SMILEY!
HEY, FONE BONE, PHONEY'S COME UP WITH A NEW PLAN TO GET US OUTTA HERE! PRETTY SOON WE'LL BE ABLE TO PAY OFF GRAN'MA BEN AN' LUCIUS, AND THEN WE CAN GO HOME!

WHAT TH' HECK IS TAKIN' YOU SO LONG?! C'MON! C'MON! YOU GOT ANY IDEA HOW HARD IT IS TO GET 'EM TO SIT IN THOSE LITTLE CHAIRS?!!

ALL SET!

I MISS THAT OL' THRILL...
GIMME GIMME GIMME! EGGS! EGGS! EGGS! I'LL BE RICH!

HEE HEE HEE HEE HEE HEE HEE HEE YES!
OH, YEAH.
HE'S ADJUSTED WELL.
I COULD BE WRONG . . .

WATCH DUTY

DID YOU HEAR THAT? THERE'S SOMEONE OUT THERE! WE'VE BEEN CAUGHT!
HOLD ON! HOLD ON! I'LL TAKE A LOOK!

WELL?
ALL CLEAR.

ARE YOU SURE? I THOUGHT I HEARD SOMETHING MOVING UP THERE!
WOULD YOU RELAX? NOBODY IS GOING TO FIND US! QUIT BEIN' SO JUMPY!

WELL, YOU'D BE JUMPY, TOO, IF YOU'D BEEN HIDING IN A HOLE IN TH' GROUND FOR FOUR DAYS!
I HAVE BEEN HIDING IN A HOLE IN TH' GROUND FOR FOUR DAYS! NOW, GO TO SLEEP!

I CAN'T! I HAVE THIS FEELING THAT WE'RE BEING WATCHED!
PROMISE ME YOU'LL KEEP CHECKING!
I HAVEN'T STOPPED CHECKING IN FOUR DAYS!! WHY DON'T YOU CHECK FOR A WHILE?!

OKAY, I WILL!

BUT IF THERE'S SOMEONE OUT THERE, IT WAS YOU WHO STARTED THAT RIOT AT THE COW RACE!
YOU'RE A PAIN IN TH' BUTT, YOU KNOW THAT?

WATCH DUTY

WASN'T ANYBODY OUT THERE, WAS THERE?

NO. BUT THERE COULD'VE BEEN.
KINGDOK WILL NEVER FIND US! WE'RE SAFE HERE! NOW SHUT UP AND GO TO SLEEP!

I CAN'T SLEEP! MY NERVES ARE SHOT! AND IT'S ALL BECAUSE OF YOU!
YOUR NERVES ARE SHOT BECAUSE YOU'RE A PAIN IN TH' BUTT!

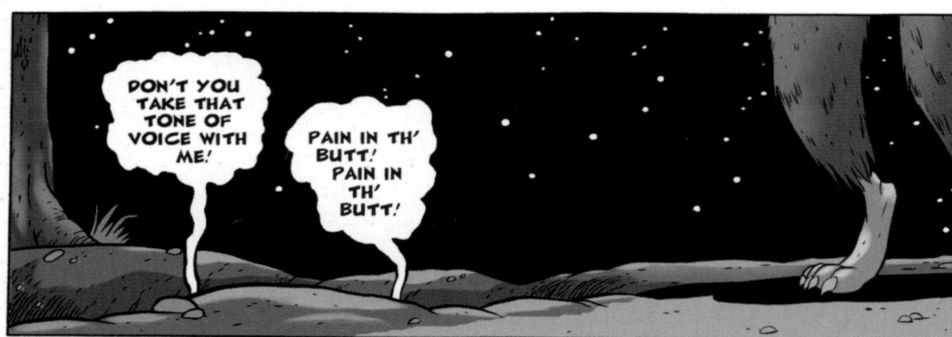
DON'T YOU TAKE THAT TONE OF VOICE WITH ME!
PAIN IN TH' BUTT! PAIN IN TH' BUTT!

Shh!
I HEARD SOMETHING! GO UP AN' LOOK!
AGAIN?! YOU JUST LOOKED!

PLEASE! PLEASE GO CHECK!
ALL RIGHT. ALL RIGHT.

WATCH DUTY

THERE! SATISFIED?! THERE'S NO ONE OUT HERE!

NOW, GO TO SLEEP, YOU BIG, FAT PAIN IN TH' - - - -

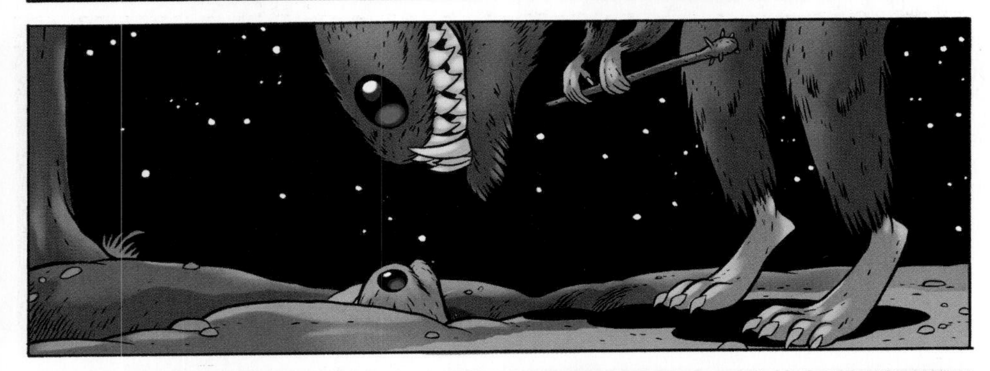

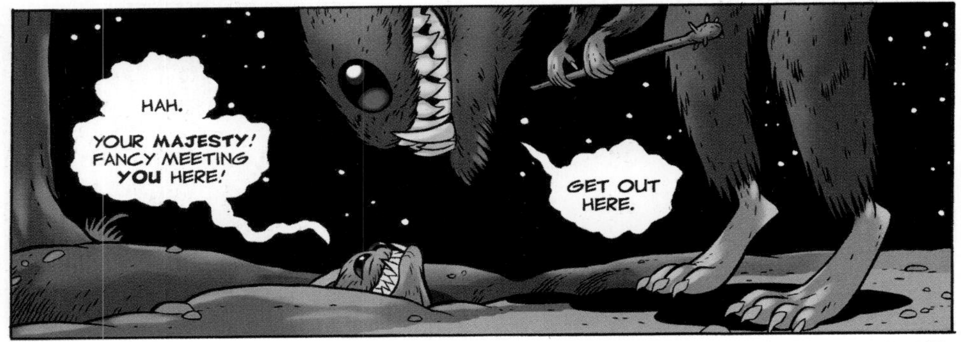
HAH.
YOUR MAJESTY! FANCY MEETING YOU HERE!
GET OUT HERE.

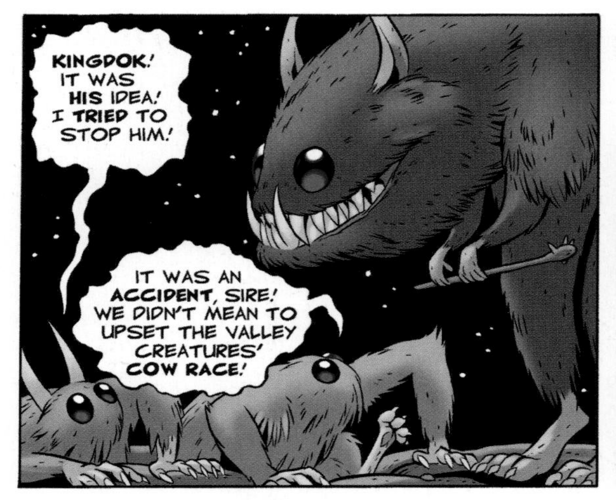
KINGDOK! IT WAS HIS IDEA! I TRIED TO STOP HIM!
IT WAS AN ACCIDENT, SIRE! WE DIDN'T MEAN TO UPSET THE VALLEY CREATURES' COW RACE!

I SHOULD KILL YOU BOTH . . .

BUT YOU KNOW WHAT? I HATE THE FLAT-LANDERS, AND I HATE THE OLD COW WOMAN, AND I REALLY HATE THOSE STUPID COW RACES!
FOR ONCE, YOU TWO MESSED UP, AND I'M HAPPY ABOUT IT!

TH - THEN . . . YOU'RE NOT GOING TO KILL US?
YOU MAY LIVE.
BUT- - BUT WHAT ABOUT TH' HOODED ONE? WE WERE UNDER ORDERS TO LAY LOW!

AM I NOT KINGDOK?! I WILL DISCIPLINE MY TROOPS THE WAY I SEE FIT!!

TAKE THIS!

WATCH DUTY

IT'S A SACK FULL OF RABBITS!
THOUGHT YOU MIGHT ENJOY A GOOD, HOT **MEAL** TONIGHT! THEY'RE ALL SKINNED AN' EVERYTHING!

HEH, HEH, HEH.
GOOD JOB, BOYS! CARRY ON!

WHAT ARE YOU DOING?
I AM LEARNING TO PLAY. THE RED DRAGON IS TEACHING ME.
HE IS A GOOD TEACHER.
AND YOU ARE PRACTICING. YOU ARE A GOOD PUPIL.

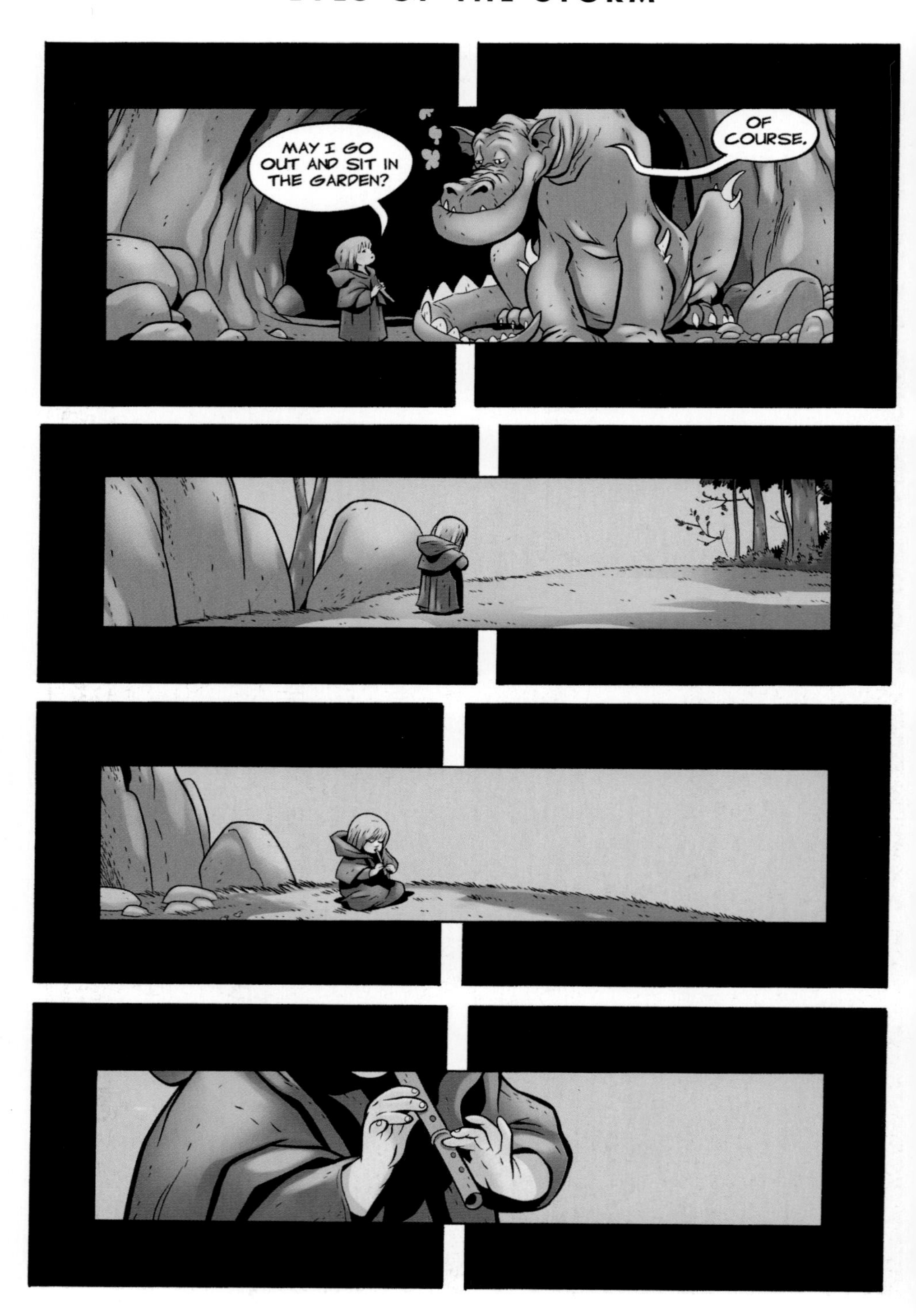
MAY I GO OUT AND SIT IN THE GARDEN?
OF COURSE.

WATCH DUTY

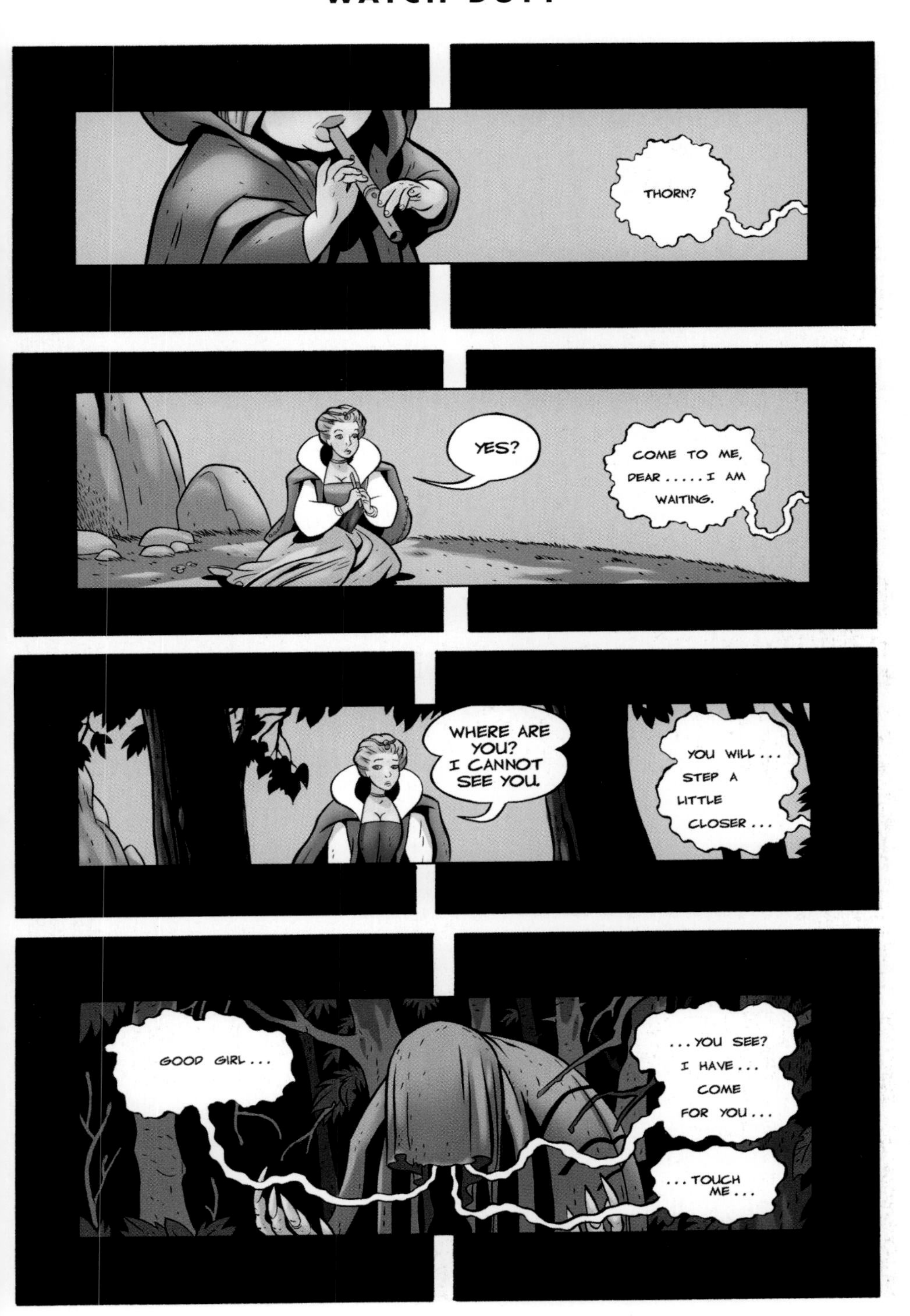
THORN?
YES?
COME TO ME, DEAR . . . . . I AM WAITING.
WHERE ARE YOU? I CANNOT SEE YOU.
YOU WILL . . . STEP A LITTLE CLOSER . . .
GOOD GIRL . . .
. . . YOU SEE? I HAVE . . . COME FOR YOU . . .
. . . TOUCH ME . . .

NO, NO, NO....
DO NOT BE FRIGHTENED....
...CLOSER... I CANNOT REACH YOU...
...ONE TOUCH...
...ONE LITTLE TOUCH....
...AND WE WILL BE TOGETHER...
PRINCESS!

WATCH DUTY

ZZK---
TWO MILES OFF TH' LEE-BEAM! A WHOLE SCHOOL OF THEM...

FONE BONE?
I FELL ASLEEP ON GUARD DUTY...
TH' BOATS! LOWER TH' BOATS!

THERE! THERE! THERE! SHE BLOWS! SHE BLOWS!

BONE
THAR SHE BLOWS! THERE! THERE!
SHE BLOWS!
THERE GO TH' FLUKES!
IS IT TH' WHITE WHALE?!
YES!
WHERE-AWAY, ISHMAEL?
ON TH' LEE-BEAM! TWO MILES OFF!
WE DON'T WANT HIM TO GET AWAY, MR. ISHMAEL! LOWER TH' BOATS!
BUT, PHONEY! MY NAME'S NOT ISHMAEL!

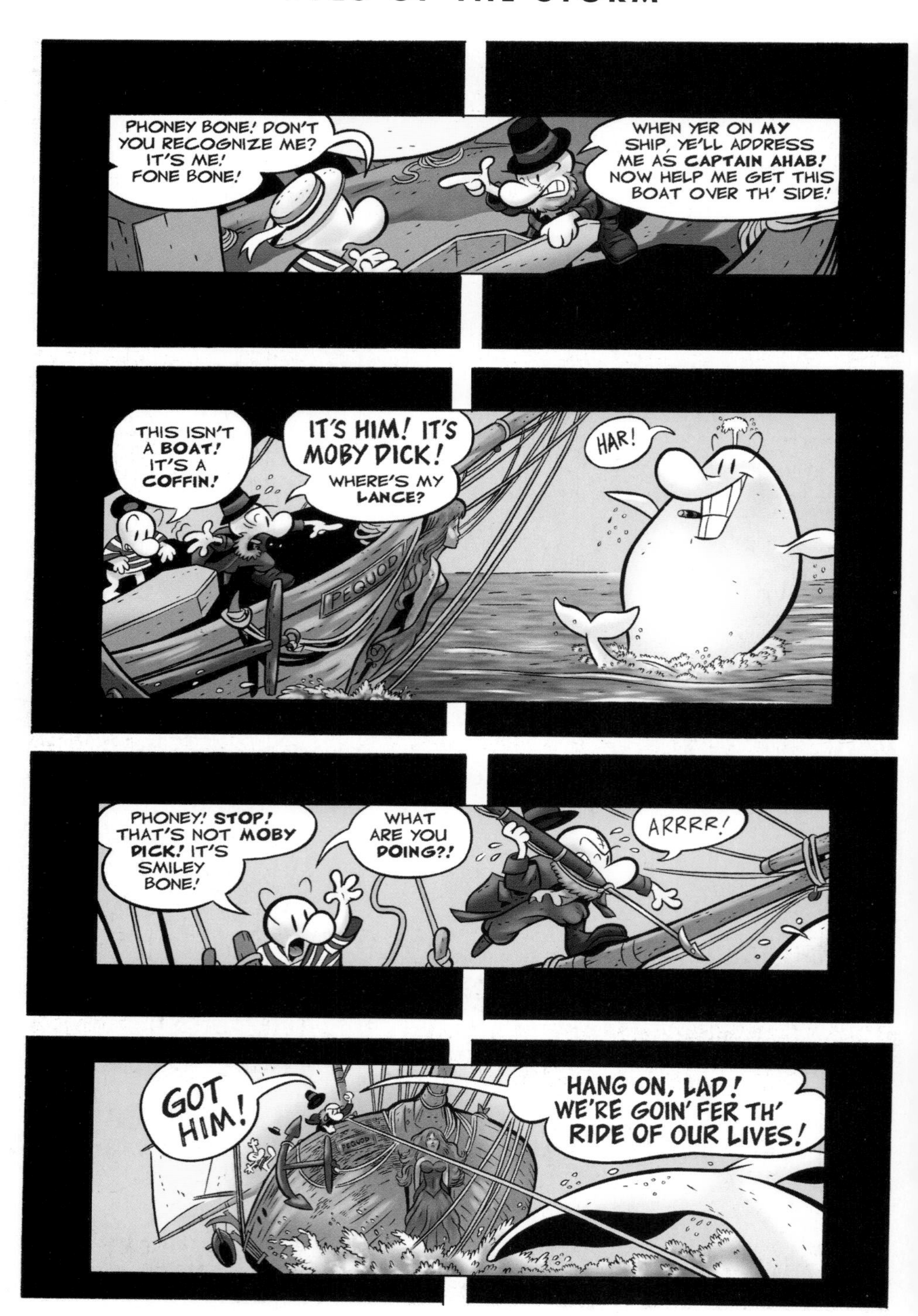

PHONEY BONE! DON'T YOU RECOGNIZE ME? IT'S ME! FONE BONE!
WHEN YER ON MY SHIP, YE'LL ADDRESS ME AS CAPTAIN AHAB! NOW HELP ME GET THIS BOAT OVER TH' SIDE!
THIS ISN'T A BOAT! IT'S A COFFIN!
IT'S HIM! IT'S MOBY DICK! WHERE'S MY LANCE?
HAR!
PEQUOD
PHONEY! STOP! THAT'S NOT MOBY DICK! IT'S SMILEY BONE!
WHAT ARE YOU DOING?!
ARRRR!
GOT HIM!
HANG ON, LAD! WE'RE GOIN' FER TH' RIDE OF OUR LIVES!

WHA-HOO-HOO HOO!
HEY! HEY! WAIT!
MAN OVERBOARD!
OHMYGOSH.
SSSSSSSSSSSSS

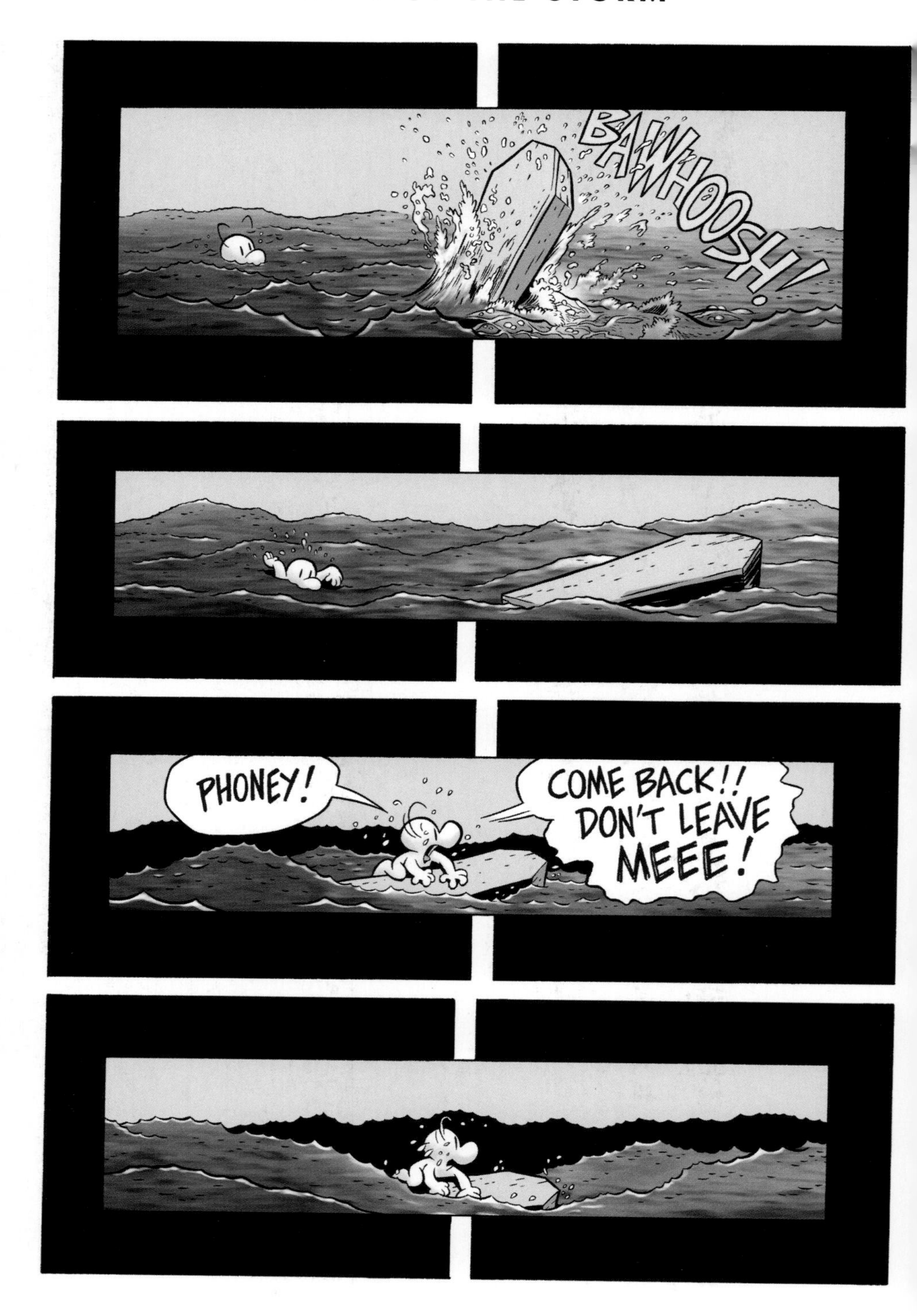
BAWHOOSH!
PHONEY!
COME BACK!! DON'T LEAVE MEEE!

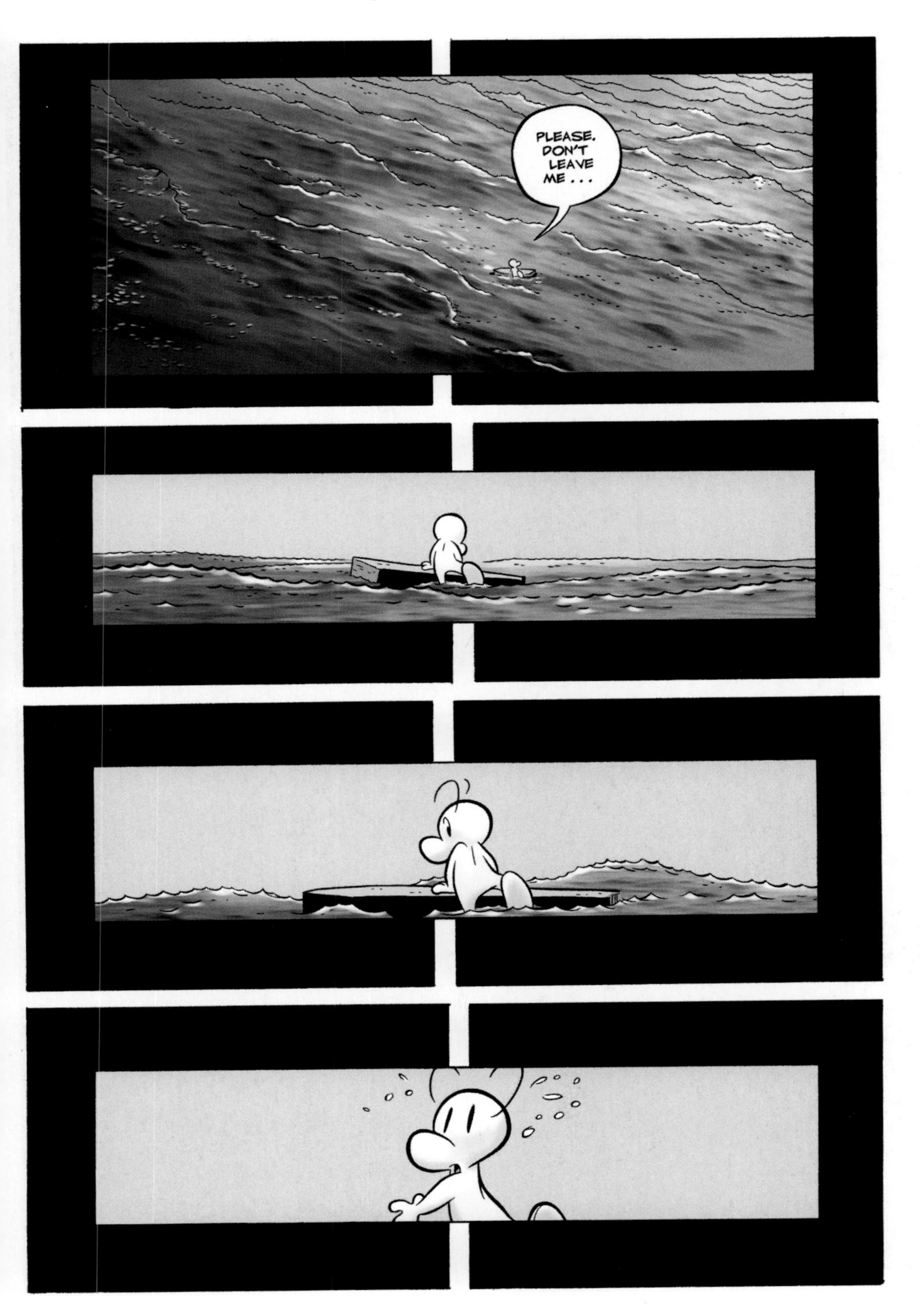
PLEASE. DON'T LEAVE ME . . .

MMMMM.
SNRK! SNRK!

UNH.

WHOA.
WHERE AM I?

JEEZ! TH' SUN'S BEEN UP FOR HOURS!

UH, OH! I OVERSLEPT!
WONDER WHERE EVERYBODY IS? PHONEY?

HELLO?
GRAN'MA? THORN?

HMMM. MUST BE OUT AN' ABOUT ALREADY!

HELLO?

HUH! NOBODY'S AROUND!
HIYA, BONE!

HEY, TED! HOW YOU DOIN', YOU OL' BUG, YOU?
PURTY GOOD! HOW 'BOUTS YOU? BEEN WORKIN' ON YER LOVE POETRYS FOR THORN?

YEAH. I'M NOT A VERY GOOD POET, THOUGH.
BOY! I'LL SAY! I READ THAT ONE YOU LEFT IN TH' FOREST!
"UPON YOUR FEET YOU HAS TEN TOES, THEY LOOKS JES LIKE PO-TA-TOES!"
PEE-YEW!

THAT ONE DOESN'T COUNT! THE RAT CREATURES INTERRUPTED ME!
YOU OUGHTA THANK 'EM! THEY DID YOU A FLAVOR!

I'LL BE SURE TO MENTION IT, NEXT TIME THEY TRY TO EAT ME!
AN' DON'T WORRY 'BOUT NO ONE ELSE READIN' THAT LOVE POETRY! I TORE THAT STINKER UP TO KINGDOM COME!

OKAY, OKAY.
I GET TH' IDEA.
SO WHAT'RE YOU DOIN' HERE, INSTEAD OF DOWN AT TH' SPRINGS FETCHIN' FRESH WATER WITH THORN?

WELL, I KINDA OVERSLEPT. I WASN'T SURE WHERE EVERYBODY WAS!
GRANNY AN' LUCIUS IS PLOWIN' UP TH' BACK FIELD, AN' THORN IS DOWN GETTIN' WATER, AN' YER COUSINS IS OFF SOMEWHERES TAKIN' A BREAK!

A BREAK? IS IT LUNCHTIME ALREADY?
HEY, TH' DAY'S HALF OVER, BONE! GET WITH IT, MAN!

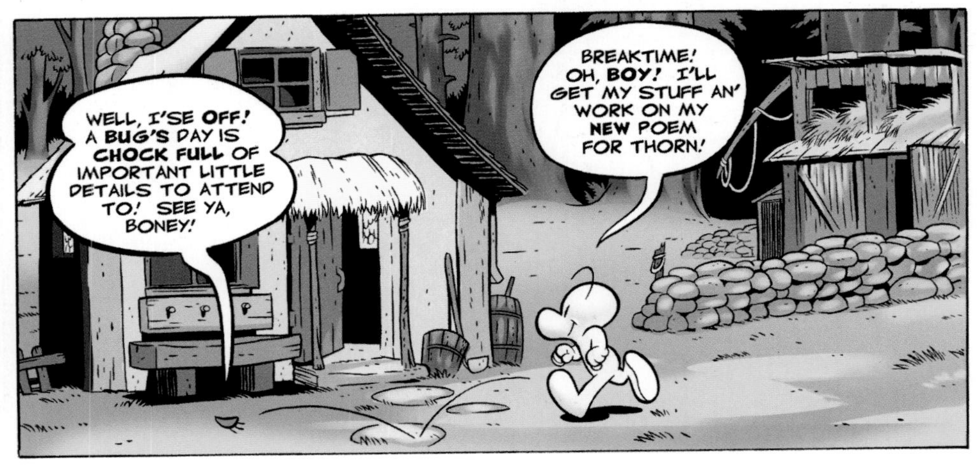
WELL, I'SE OFF! A BUG'S DAY IS CHOCK FULL OF IMPORTANT LITTLE DETAILS TO ATTEND TO! SEE YA, BONEY!
BREAKTIME! OH, BOY! I'LL GET MY STUFF AN' WORK ON MY NEW POEM FOR THORN!

NOW TO FIND A NICE, QUIET SPOT TO WRITE!

PREFERABLY SOMEPLACE PRIVATE!

THIS LOOKS GOOD! A SUN-DRENCHED MEADOW BESPECKLED WITH WILD FLOWERS, AN' TH' AIR FILLED WITH WAFTED SCENTS OF HONEYSUCKLE AN' MARIGOLDS!

YEAH, YEAH! THIS IS TH' PERFECT PLACE TO WORK ON MY ULTIMATE EXPRESSION OF LOVE FOR THORN! LET'S SEE . . . A ROSE IS A ROSE IS A . . . HUM TE DUM . . .
. . . A ROSE! RIGHT!

HMM, HMM, MMMM. HMMM.
OH, YES! THIS IS GOOD! THIS IS REAL GOOD!
I WONDER WHAT RHYMES WITH SMOOTH, BROWN THIGH?

HI, FONE BONE! WHATCHA WORKIN' ON?

NUTHIN'!
UH . . .
NEED SOME HELP WITH THAT WATER?
NO, THAT'S OKAY. I'VE GOT IT . . .

SO . . . DO YOU REMEMBER YOUR DREAM?
WHAT?

YESTERDAY YOU TOLD ME YOU COULDN'T REMEMBER A SINGLE DREAM YOU'VE HAD SINCE COMING TO THE VALLEY - - WELL, THIS MORNING WHEN I SAW YOU WERE HAVING A DREAM, I LET YOU SLEEP IN!

OH!
YEAH! I DID HAVE A DREAM!
WHAT WAS IT ABOUT?

UM . . . IT WAS WEIRD! I WAS ON A SHIP - -
AN' RIGHT BEFORE I WOKE UP, THE DRAGON ROSE UP OUT OF TH' OCEAN! AN' HE WAS BIG!

I MEAN HUGE! LIKE A MOUNTAIN! AN' HE WAS LOOKIN' AT ME WITH THESE REALLY INTENSE EYES!
I HAD A STRANGE VISITOR IN MY DREAMS LAST NIGHT, TOO! AND HE LOOKED LIKE YOU!

REALLY? YOU HAD A DREAM ABOUT ME?
IT LOOKED LIKE YOU, BUT IT DIDN'T FEEL LIKE YOU. I DON'T THINK OUR TWO DREAMS ARE A COINCIDENCE!

I CAN'T BELIEVE IT!! YOU HAD A DREAM ABOUT ME!
HEE HEE HEE!
WE SHOULD TALK ABOUT THIS TONIGHT, OKAY?

OKAY! GOSH! WHAT WAS TH' DREAM ABOUT? IF YOU DON'T MIND ME ASKIN'?

WAIT! BEFORE YOU TELL ME! HERE! HAVE SOME VIOLETS! THEY'LL LOOK SO LOVELY NEXT TO YOUR EYES!

HOO, HEE... I HOPE YOU DON'T THINK I'M BEING TOO FORWARD...
NOT AT ALL.

MY, WHAT A BEAUTIFUL BARITONE VOICE YOU HAVE.
DON'T YOU THINK DAISIES WOULD HAVE SET OFF MY EYES BETTER?

SIGH.
LOVE LIFE HASN'T IMPROVED MUCH, HAS IT?

NO. NOT THAT IT'S ANY OF YOUR BUSINESS!
FAIR ENOUGH. I'LL BE ON MY WAY.

HEY, WAIT A MINUTE, DRAGON! YOU GOTTA HEAR ABOUT THIS DREAM I HAD LAST NIGHT! YOU WERE IN IT!

I SAW THIS GIANT IMAGE OF YOUR HEAD! YOU DIDN'T SAY ANYTHING- YOU WERE JUST STARIN' AT ME! WHAT DO YOU THINK? YOU THINK IT'S WEIRD THAT I'D HAVE A DREAM LIKE THAT?
NO.

THORN HAD AN INTRUDER IN HER DREAMS LAST NIGHT.
SO DID YOU.

WELCOME ABOARD, ISHMAEL.

HEY, YOU! NOW JUST A MINUTE--- DON'T YOU ISHMAEL ME!!

YOU---! YOU---!

STAY OUTTA MY DREAMS!

I MEAN IT!!

MAN!
THAT IS SPOOKY! THAT IS REALLY SPOOKY!

HOW TH' HECK DID HE KNOW I WAS ISHMAEL IN THAT DREAM? THAT'S IMPOSSIBLE! IT'S A COINCIDENCE!

DON'T THINK ABOUT IT.
NOW, WHERE WAS I?

A ROSE IS A ROSE IS A ROSE . . .

OH, YEAH! MY MASTERPIECE!
HMM, HMM.

HOWDY, FONE BONE! FINALLY GOT UP, I SEE!
HEY, GUYS. WHATCHA UP TO?

AS LITTLE AS WE CAN GET AWAY WITH! WHAT'RE YOU DOIN'? WRITIN' SOMETHIN'?
ME?
NO.
LEMME SEE THAT!

HEY!
WELL. WELL, WHAT HAVE WE HERE? POETRY! MISSIVES OF LOVE TO OUR DEAR AND INCREDIBLY GOOD-LOOKING FRIEND THORN!

GIMME THAT!!
"A ROSE IS A ROSE IS A ROSE, BUT YOU, MY SWEET PETUNIA, IS A ROSE THAT MY NOSE ONLY KNOWS!"
WHAT'S THAT SUPPOSED TO MEAN?

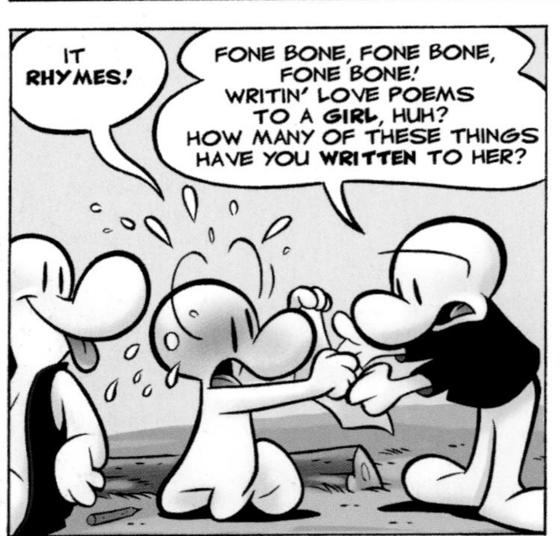
IT RHYMES!
FONE BONE, FONE BONE, FONE BONE! WRITIN' LOVE POEMS TO A GIRL, HUH? HOW MANY OF THESE THINGS HAVE YOU WRITTEN TO HER?

A COUPLE HUNDRED.
JEEZ! THORN MUST THINK YOU'RE A DROOLING IDIOT BY NOW!

SHE DOES NOT!!

I NEVER SHOWED 'EM TO HER.
WIMP!

YOU'RE LETTIN' THESE WOMEN-FOLK GET TO YA, FONE BONE!
WHAT DO YOU MEAN?

I SEE HOW YOU JUMP WHENEVER THORN WANTS YOU TO DO SOMETHING!
OH, FONE BONE, HELP ME CARRY THE WATER! OH, FONE BONE, IT'S TIME TO DO TH' LAUNDRY!

PHONEY! GRAN'MA BEN AND THORN ARE GIVING US A PLACE TO LIVE! WE HAVE TO HELP OUT WITH TH' CHORES!

OH, YEAH? WELL, YOU DON'T SEE ME AN' SMILEY DROP EVERYTHING AN' GO RUNNIN' EVERY TIME THORN AN' GRAN'MA BEN SNAP THEIR FINGERS!

DING! DING! DING! DING!
OBOY! IT'S TH' DINNER BELL!
HANG ON, GRAN'MA! WE'RE COMIN'!

HOLD IT, BOYS! NOT IN TH' HOUSE! I WANT YA BACK IN TH' YARD WITH ME!
OOF!
WHAM!
OW!

WHAT GIVES, GRAN'MA?
YEAH, WHAT'S GOIN' ON? IT'S WAY TOO EARLY FOR DINNER!

I DIDN'T CALL YA TO EAT DINNER, YA IDIOTS! I WANT YA TO MAKE DINNER!
SEE? WHAT'D I TELL YOU? WOMEN AIN'T NOTHIN' BUT TROUBLE!

FILL THIS KETTLE WITH WATER AND BRING IT BACK TO TH' CHICKEN COOP! AN' BUILD A FIRE UNDER IT. I NEED THAT WATER BOILIN', YOU GOT THAT?
YES, MA'AM!

YOU TWO COME WITH ME.

I WANT YOU BOYS TO CATCH YOURSELVES FOUR CHICKENS! WHEN SMILEY'S GOT THAT WATER GOIN' NICE AN' HOT, DIP TH' BIRDS IN IT! I WANT EVERY ONE OF THEM FEATHERS GONE, SO SOAK 'EM GOOD! I BETTER BE SMELLIN' WET FEATHERS BACK HERE!

POO! THERE'S A SMELL YOU DON'T FORGET TOO QUICK!
OHMYGOSH.
WE'RE GONNA BOIL 'EM ALIVE?!

OF COURSE NOT, DEAR. YOU'RE GONNA CUT THEIR HEADS OFF FIRST.
WITH WHAT?

WITH TH' HATCHET.
UH . . .
ARE THEY GONNA . . . Y'KNOW . . . RUN AROUND TH' YARD? SQUIRTIN' BLOOD AN' STUFF?

WHAT'S TH' MATTER? AIN'T YOU BOYS EVER CHOPPED TH' HEAD OFF A CHICKEN BEFORE?
UH . . .
UH . . .

OH, FER HEAVEN'S SAKES! IF YA CAN'T HANDLE A LITTLE FLAPPIN' AROUND, JUST GRAB TH' CHICKEN BY TH' NECK AN' GIVE HER A GOOD CRANK OVER YOUR HEAD -- THAT'LL KILL HER FIRST!

MMMMP!

FLOP!

HMMF.
CITY BOYS!

BONE
ALL RIGHT, YOU LAZY BONES! WAKE IT UP!
WE'RE HEADIN' BACK TO BARRELHAVEN, AN' I WANNA GET AN EARLY START!
TODAY?! RIGHT NOW? AW, JEEZ! IT'S STILL DARK OUT!
WE'RE GOIN' FOR A RIDE?!
THAT'S RIGHT! ALL TH' CHORES ARE DONE - - ALL THE SPRING PLANTING'S DONE - - AND YOU KNOW WHAT THAT MEANS! YOU TWO ARE COMIN' WITH ME TO START WORKIN' OFF THAT 100 TO 1 LONGSHOT BET!
AS OF THIS MOMENT, YOU BOYS ARE MINE!
I HATE IT WHEN HE DOES THAT.

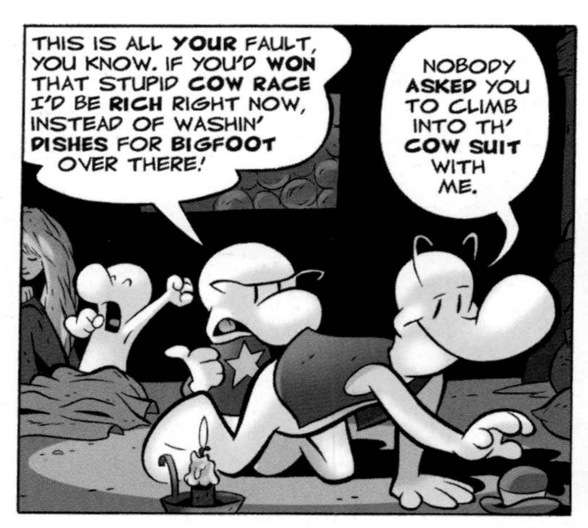
THIS IS ALL YOUR FAULT, YOU KNOW. IF YOU'D WON THAT STUPID COW RACE I'D BE RICH RIGHT NOW, INSTEAD OF WASHIN' DISHES FOR BIGFOOT OVER THERE!
NOBODY ASKED YOU TO CLIMB INTO TH' COW SUIT WITH ME.

WHAT ELSE WAS I GONNA DO?! I CAN'T TRUST YOU TO DO ANYTHING RIGHT!!
BALLAST! THAT'S ALL YOU WERE!
B-A-L-A-S-S-T!

KNOCK IT OFF! YOU TWO BETTER NOT CRAP AROUND LIKE THIS TH' WHOLE WAY TO BARRELHAVEN! NOW, C'MON, LET'S GO!
YEAH, YEAH. ARE WE GONNA EAT BREAKFAST FIRST, OR WHAT?

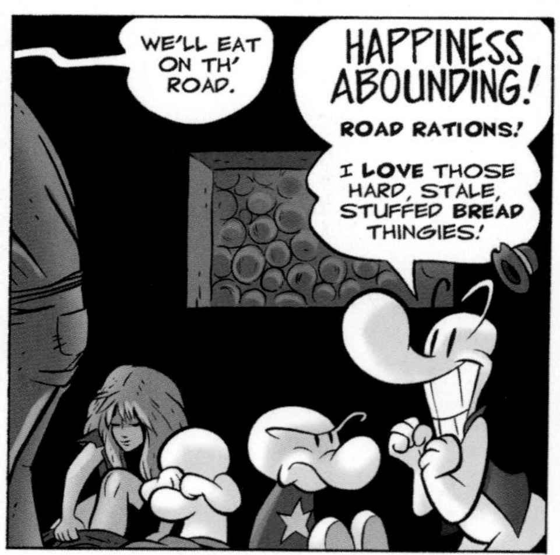
WE'LL EAT ON TH' ROAD.
HAPPINESS ABOUNDING!
ROAD RATIONS!
I LOVE THOSE HARD, STALE, STUFFED BREAD THINGIES!

HOW DID YOU SLEEP LAST NIGHT, FONE BONE?
I DIDN'T HAVE ANY MORE WEIRD DREAMS. WHAT ABOUT YOU?

EVERYBODY OUTSIDE!
MOVE IT! MOVE IT!
I SLEPT PRETTY HARD. NO NEW DREAMS FOR ME, EITHER.
RRRR.

GOOD MORNING, EVERYONE! MY! DON'T WE LOOK BRIGHT AND BUSHY-TAILED!
WE'RE ALL READY TO GO, ROSIE.
HEY, GRAN'MA! DID YOU PACK ANY OF THOSE HARD, LITTLE, STUFFED BREAD THINGIES FOR ME?

OF COURSE, DEAR. I MADE THEM TWO DAYS AGO, SO THEY'D BE EXTRA STALE - - JUST TH' WAY YOU LIKE 'EM!
YES!
RRRR.

WHAT DO YOU THINK, ROSE? IS TH' WEATHER GONNA HOLD?
IT'S TOO EARLY TO SAY. IT MAY RAIN BEFORE YOU GET TO TH' VILLAGE.

BETTER GET STARTED, THEN.
OKAY! TIME TO GO!

PHONEY! YOU AND SMILEY BONE GET IN TH' CART. WHAT ABOUT YOU, FONE BONE? YOU WANNA STAY WITH ME AN' THORN, OR GO WITH YOUR COUSINS?
I GET TO CHOOSE?

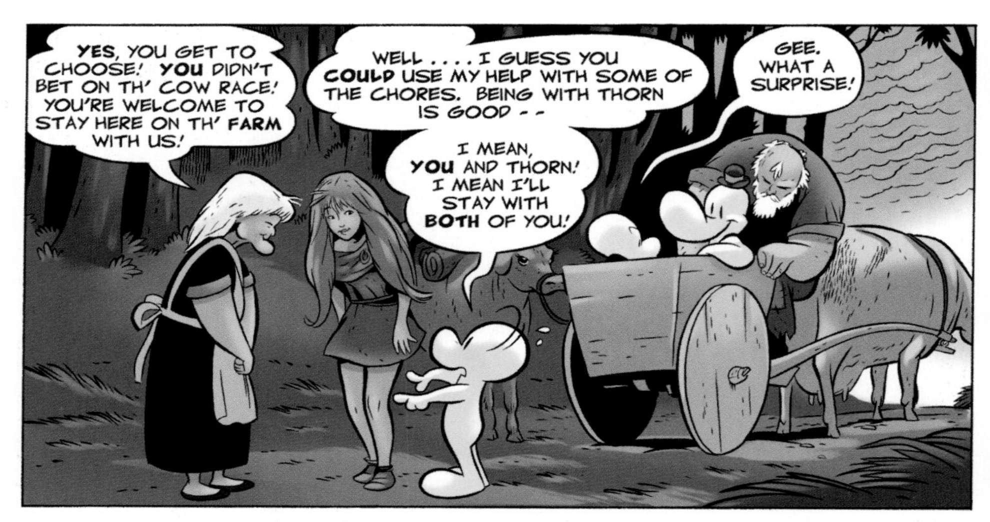
YES, YOU GET TO CHOOSE! YOU DIDN'T BET ON TH' COW RACE! YOU'RE WELCOME TO STAY HERE ON TH' FARM WITH US!
WELL . . . . I GUESS YOU COULD USE MY HELP WITH SOME OF THE CHORES. BEING WITH THORN IS GOOD - -
I MEAN, YOU AND THORN! I MEAN I'LL STAY WITH BOTH OF YOU!
GEE. WHAT A SURPRISE!

GOOD-BYE, BOYS! KEEP A SHARP LOOKOUT ON TH' ROAD!
WE'LL BE BACK IN A FEW DAYS, ROSE. TAKE CARE OF YOURSELF.

SEE YA LATER, GUYS!
BITE ME.

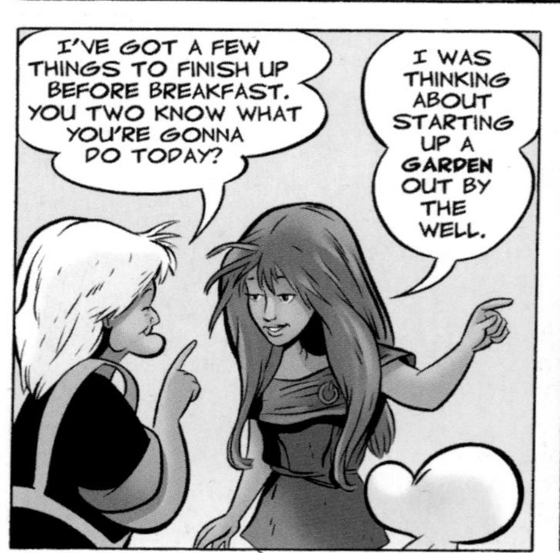
I'VE GOT A FEW THINGS TO FINISH UP BEFORE BREAKFAST. YOU TWO KNOW WHAT YOU'RE GONNA DO TODAY?
I WAS THINKING ABOUT STARTING UP A GARDEN OUT BY THE WELL.

THAT'S A FINE IDEA! BUT FEED TH' CHICKENS FIRST!
OKAY! C'MON, FONE BONE!

LET'S PLAY A GAME!
NO.

LET'S TALK ABOUT YOU!
NO.
AND GET THAT CIGAR OUTTA MY FACE!

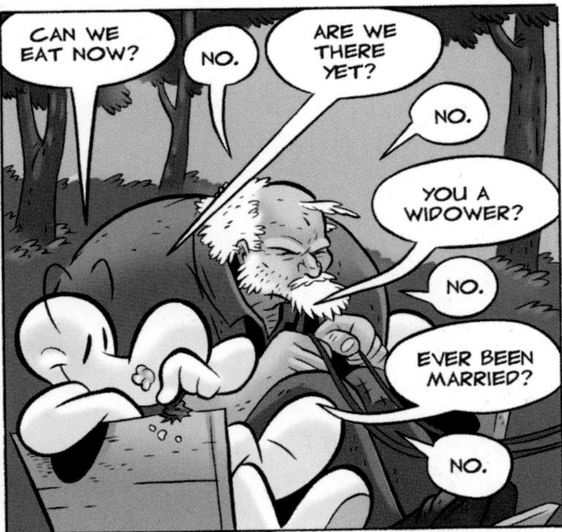
CAN WE EAT NOW?
NO.
ARE WE THERE YET?
NO.
YOU A WIDOWER?
NO.
EVER BEEN MARRIED?
NO.

I ALMOST GOT MARRIED ONCE.

REALLY?!
IT WAS A LONG TIME AGO.... SHE WAS A BEAUTIFUL WOMAN -- TH' MOST BEAUTIFUL WOMAN IN TH' WHOLE VALLEY...

WE WERE IN LOVE, AND WE COURTED. A LOT OF FOLKS THOUGHT WE WERE GONNA GET HITCHED...

SO WHAT HAPPENED? WHY DIDN'T YOU GET MARRIED?

SHE DIDN'T WANT TO.
HMM. THAT STORM IS BLOWIN' IN A LOT FASTER THAN I THOUGHT.

UH, OH!
WE GOT TROUBLE!

THERE'S SOMEONE FOLLOWING US!

WHERE? I DON'T SEE ANYTHING!
IT WENT INTO TH' BUSHES! IT WAS A RAT CREATURE!

ARE YOU SURE? MAYBE IT WAS TH' WIND BLOWIN' TH' BUSHES AROUND . . .
HEY! I THOUGHT GRAN'MA BEN SAID IT WAS SAFE TO MAKE THIS TRIP!!

ROSE ISN'T ALWAYS RIGHT. WE'RE FAR ENOUGH AWAY FROM TH' DRAGON'S PROTECTION THAT THEY MIGHT ATTACK US . . .
. . . BUT THAT MEANS WE'RE CUT OFF! WE HAVE TO MAKE IT TO TH' VILLAGE ON OUR OWN!

SMILEY! GET OUT AND RIDE TH' EXTRA COW - - IF WE HAVE TO MAKE A RUN FOR IT, WE NEED TO LIGHTEN UP TH' CART!

♪
LOOKS LIKE A STORM IS BLOWING IN.

HEY, CHECK THESE ROCKS OUT - - THEY HAVE LITTLE CARVINGS ALL OVER THEM.
LET ME SEE.

YEAH! THESE ARE GRAN'MA'S GOOD LUCK CHARMS SHE BROUGHT WITH HER FROM THE SOUTH.

SHE SAYS IT'S A CUSTOM WHERE SHE COMES FROM TO KEEP THEM IN YOUR GARDEN.

WELL, YOU CAN'T HAVE TOO MUCH GOOD LUCK.
BE SURE THEY FACE OUT, OR ELSE THEY WON'T WARD OFF GHOST CIRCLES!

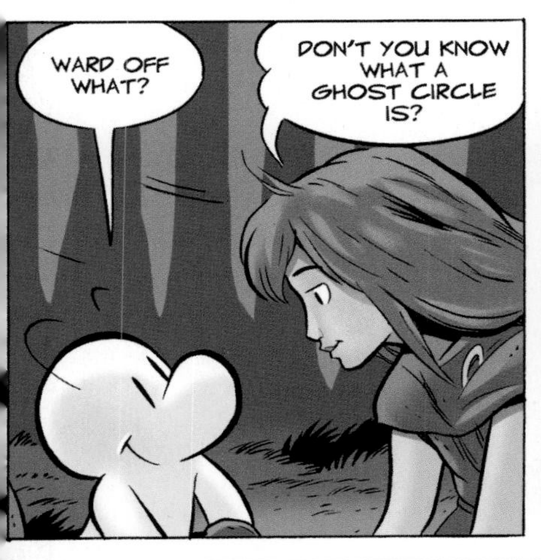
WARD OFF WHAT?
DON'T YOU KNOW WHAT A GHOST CIRCLE IS?

NO.
HAVE YOU EVER WALKED IN THE WOODS AT NIGHT AND COME ACROSS A COLD SPOT? AND SUDDENLY A CHILL RUNS UP YOUR SPINE?

YEAH . . . I THINK I HAVE.
THAT'S A GHOST CIRCLE!

THEY'RE SUPPOSED TO BE OPENINGS TO THE SPIRIT WORLD. I GUESS IN THE OLD DAYS, THEY WERE PRETTY DANGEROUS.

NO KIDDING.
I HEARD A STORY ONCE THAT A LITTLE GIRL STEPPED INTO A GHOST CIRCLE AND WAS NEVER HEARD FROM AGAIN!

PLINK!

I FELT A DROP!
I THINK TH' STORM IS GONNA START!
HERE IT COMES!
RUN FOR THE BARN!

KRAK BOOM!

WHOA! WE GOT CREAMED!
IT ONLY RAINED ON US FOR A MOMENT, AND I'M SOAKED!

LET'S SIT DOWN.
I LOVE BEING IN THE BARN WHEN IT STORMS.

LISTEN TO ALL THE DROPS HITTING THE ROOF.
LOOK OUTSIDE! IT'S LIKE NIGHT OUT THERE!

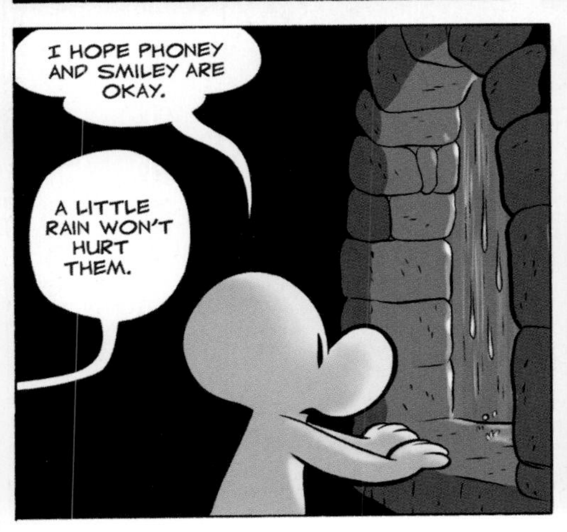
I HOPE PHONEY AND SMILEY ARE OKAY.
A LITTLE RAIN WON'T HURT THEM.

I WASN'T THINKING ABOUT THE RAIN.

I'M SURE THEY'RE SAFE. LUCIUS WILL PROTECT THEM . . .

. . . OR THE DRAGON WILL.

WELL, C'MON. THERE'S SOMETHING WE HAVE TO DO.
THERE IS?

IT'S TIME TO TALK ABOUT THE DREAMS . . .

KREEEEEEK
GROOANN
YOU LOOK A LITTLE NERVOUS, BONE.
I DON'T KNOW WHAT'S WORSE! WAITIN' FOR TH' RAT CREATURES, OR WAITIN' FOR TH' WIND TO BLOW A TREE DOWN ON OUR HEADS!

DON'T WORRY ABOUT TH' TREES. THEY'VE STOOD UP TO WORSE THAN THIS --
CRACK

R-R-R-R-R-R-R-R-R-R
SSHHHSHS
SNAP!
CRAK!

CRASSH!
OH, YEAH?! THAT WAS A TREE FALLIN' DOWN SOMEWHERE! AN' CLOSE, TOO! WORRIED ABOUT IT NOW, MR. SMARTY PANTS?

THAT TREE WAS UP AHEAD.
SOMEBODY JUST BLOCKED OUR PATH.
LUCIUS!

WHAT DO I DO? WHAT DO I DO?
WALK YOUR COW OVER TO US . . . BUT DO IT SLOWLY. DON'T MAKE ANY SUDDEN MOVES.

HERE. TAKE THIS KNIFE AN' KEEP YER HEAD DOWN . . . I'M GONNA TRY TO STALL 'EM SO SMILEY CAN GET PAST US . . .

HAIRY MEN!
WHY HAVE YOU STOPPED US?!
SSSSSSSSS

SSSSS
GIVE US THE CREATURE . . .
. . . WITH THE STAR ON ITS CHEST . . .

. . . GIVE IT TO US . . .
. . AND WE WILL LET YOU GO ON YOUR WAY . . . .

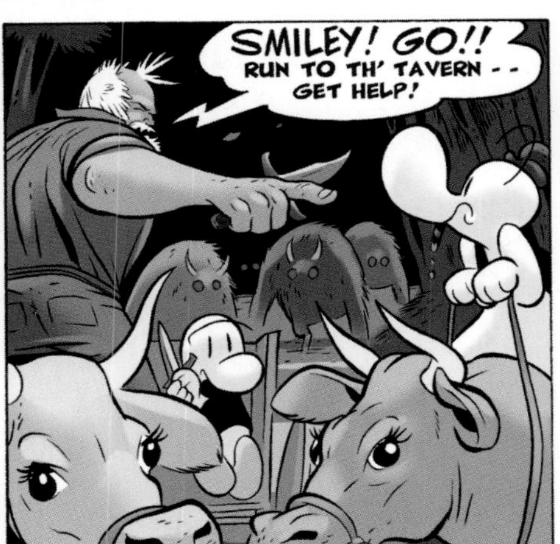
SMILEY! GO!! RUN TO TH' TAVERN - - GET HELP!

TOO LATE!

SMACK

YEEE-HAW!
OOF!
STOP THEM!

THE REINS!
WHAT?

GET TH' REINS!!

BAM!

CRUNCH

OH, NO!
WHAT?! WHAT?!

OLD MAN'S CAVE!!

YIP! YIP! YIP!

YIP! YIP! YIP! YIP!

WOO! WOO!

SMILEY! YOU SAVED US!
YAH HOO!

SMILEY! THE CLIFF!!

I'M WITH YA!
GIT ALONG LI'L DAWGIE! YAH! YAH!

YAAAAAAA

AAAAA

GAAH!
SPUT! SPUTTER!

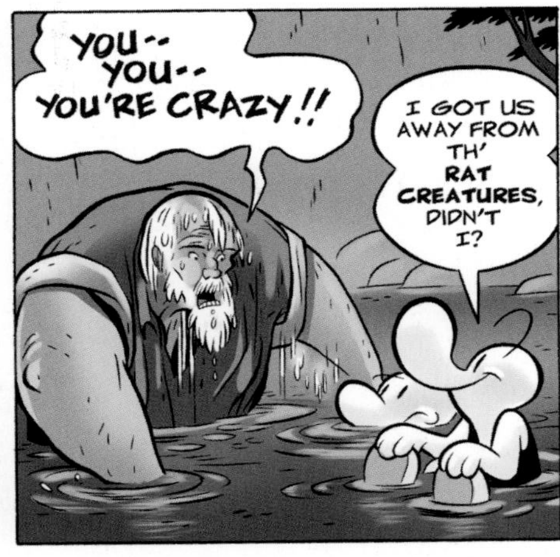
YOU-- YOU-- YOU'RE CRAZY!!
I GOT US AWAY FROM TH' RAT CREATURES, DIDN'T I?

RRRRRRRFF!
YEAH.
YOU DID DO THAT.

KRAK BOOM!

IS EVERYTHING I DO WITH YOU TWO BOYS GONNA BE LIKE THIS?
LIKE WHAT?

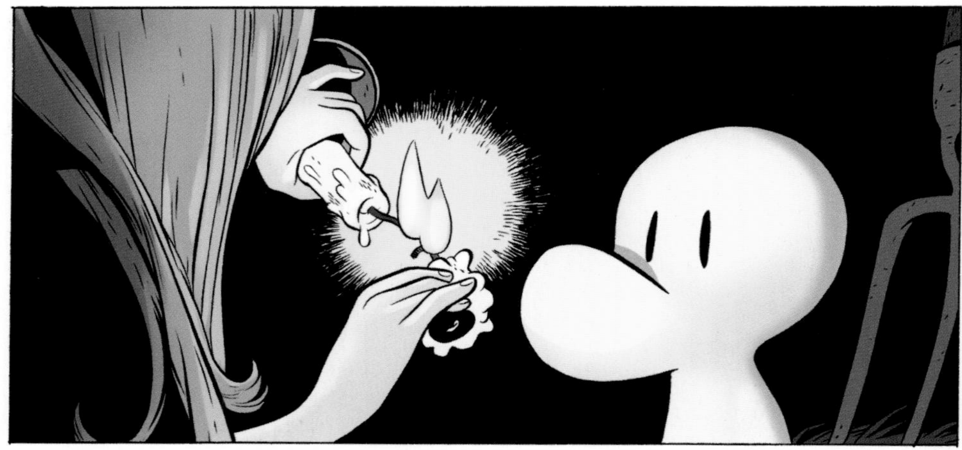

DREAMS ARE WINDOWS TO THE SPIRIT WORLD...
THAT'S WHAT OUR ANCESTORS BELIEVED.
A WORLD FROM WHICH EVERYONE COMES...
...AND TO WHICH EVERYONE MUST ONE DAY RETURN.

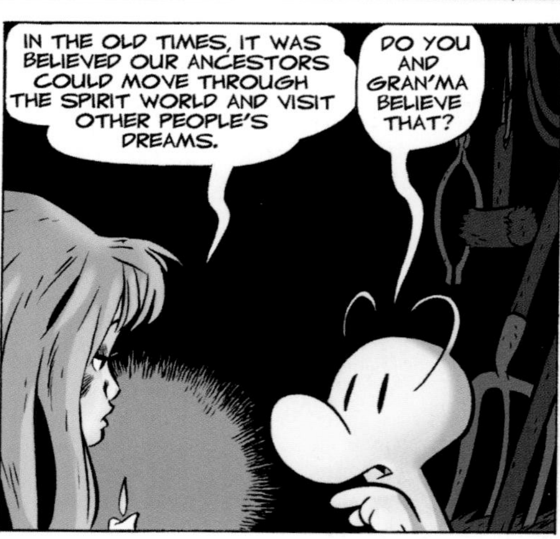
IN THE OLD TIMES, IT WAS BELIEVED OUR ANCESTORS COULD MOVE THROUGH THE SPIRIT WORLD AND VISIT OTHER PEOPLE'S DREAMS.
DO YOU AND GRAN'MA BELIEVE THAT?

I'M NOT SURE. GRAN'MA NEVER LIKED TO TALK ABOUT DREAMS. ESPECIALLY MY DREAMS ABOUT DRAGONS.
WELL, I DON'T KNOW ANYTHING ABOUT SPIRIT WORLDS, BUT IT SURE SEEMS LIKE THE DRAGON PAID ME A VISIT THE OTHER NIGHT...

HIS HEAD APPEARED IN MY DREAM BREAKING THROUGH THE SURFACE OF THE OCEAN... WHEN I TOLD HIM ABOUT IT THE NEXT DAY, HE SAYS, WELCOME ABOARD, ISHMAEL!
ONLY THE WEIRD THING IS I NEVER TOLD HIM THE DREAM WAS ABOUT MOBY DICK!

HE SAID ISHMAEL? HE KNEW YOUR DREAM WAS ABOUT MOBY DICK?
SCARY, HUH? HOW'D HE KNOW WHAT I WAS DREAMING ABOUT?
AND HE KNEW ABOUT THAT CREEPY GUY IN YOUR DREAM, TOO! SO WHO WAS THAT?

IN MY DREAM? I DON'T KNOW . . .
IT WAS A HOODED FIGURE. WHOEVER - - OR WHATEVER - - IT WAS, I WAS VERY FRIGHTENED.
HM. AND YOU SAID HE HAD MY FACE.

HE HAD YOUR FACE, BUT I THINK . . . HE WAS JUST USING IT TO LURE ME TO HIM.
AND A GROUP OF HOODED PEOPLE WERE TAKING YOU OVER THE MOUNTAINS TO LIVE WITH THE DRAGONS . . .

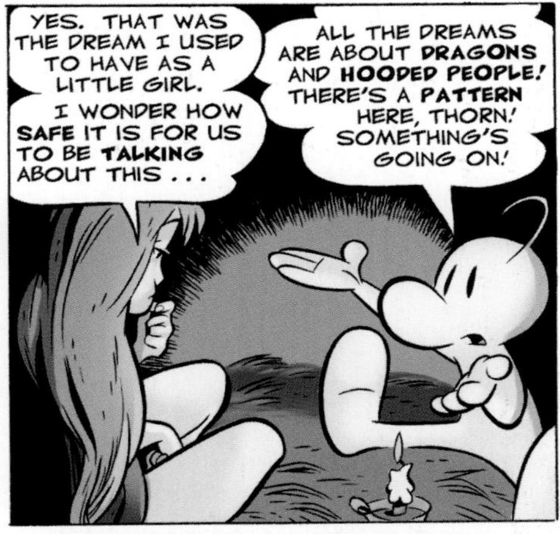
YES. THAT WAS THE DREAM I USED TO HAVE AS A LITTLE GIRL.
I WONDER HOW SAFE IT IS FOR US TO BE TALKING ABOUT THIS . . .
ALL THE DREAMS ARE ABOUT DRAGONS AND HOODED PEOPLE! THERE'S A PATTERN HERE, THORN! SOMETHING'S GOING ON!

DID YOU HEAR SOME-THING?
GRAN'MA BEN KNOWS THE TRUTH ABOUT WHERE YOU WERE RAISED! HOW COME SHE'S NEVER TOLD YOU? INSTEAD, SHE TOLD YOU THAT DRAGONS AREN'T REAL - -

CREEAK

BONE
KRAK KK POW!
GRAN'MA?
ARE YOU ALL RIGHT?
MAN! SHE DOESN'T LOOK TOO GOOD.
GRAN'MA, YOU . . . YOU SCARED US! WE DIDN'T HEAR YOU COME IN THE BARN - -

KEEE-RA-

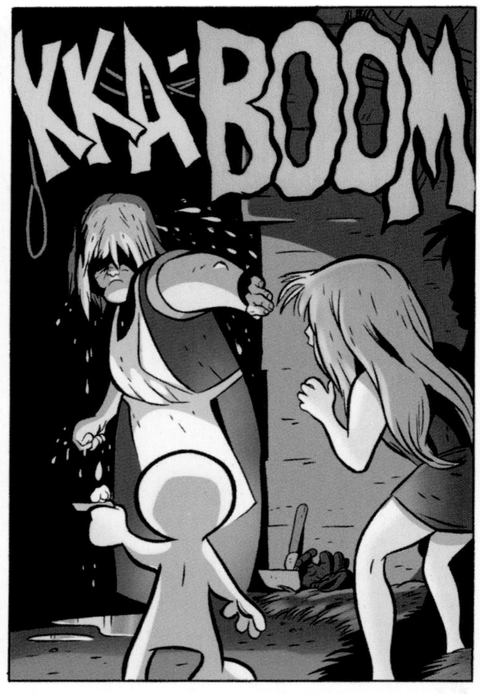
KKA-BOOM

WHAT TH' HECK WAS THAT ALL ABOUT?!
I DON'T KNOW. SHE LOOKED REALLY UPSET.
DO YOU THINK SHE OVERHEARD US TALKING ABOUT OUR DREAMS?

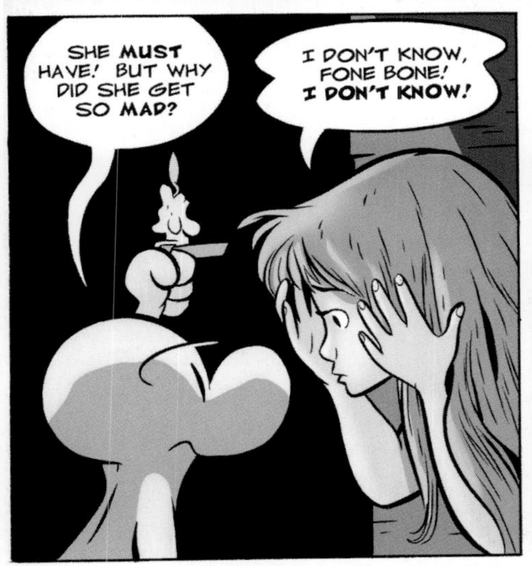
SHE MUST HAVE! BUT WHY DID SHE GET SO MAD?
I DON'T KNOW, FONE BONE! I DON'T KNOW!

WELL, I DO! SOMEONE'S BEEN PLAYIN' AROUND IN OUR HEADS GIVIN' US NIGHTMARES, AN' YOUR GRANDMOTHER KNOWS SOMETHIN' ABOUT IT!

C'MON! WE GOTTA CATCH HER!

KRACK
BOOM

FONE BONE! WAIT!

SHE'S NOT IN THE HOUSE!
SHE'S GOING INTO THE WOODS!

KKRAK
YIKES!

BABOOM
WHOA! THAT LIGHTNING WAS CLOSE!

OKAY, I GIVE! LET'S GO BACK TO TH' HOUSE!

THORN!
WE CAN'T STAY OUT HERE! IT'S TOO DANGEROUS!
I'M GONNA FIND GRAN'MA BEN!
GRAN'MA!

WE'LL NEVER FIND HER! WE CAN'T EVEN SEE TWO FEET IN FRONT OF US!

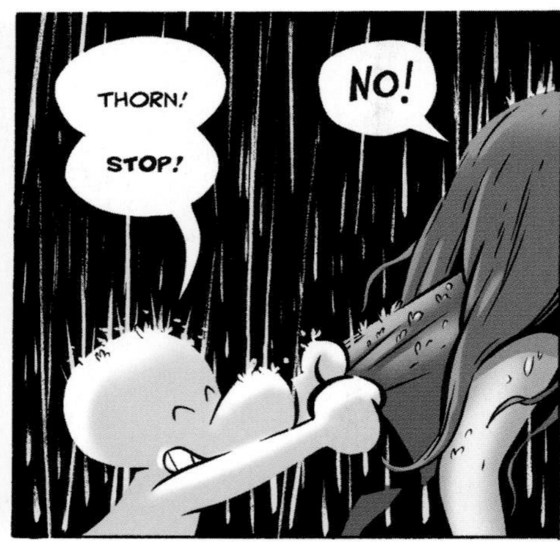
THORN!
STOP!
NO!

SHE WAS HEADED THIS WAY! WE'LL FIND HER!

KRAAKKLE!

GRAN'MA!

YOU SCARED US HALF TO DEATH! ARE YOU OKAY?

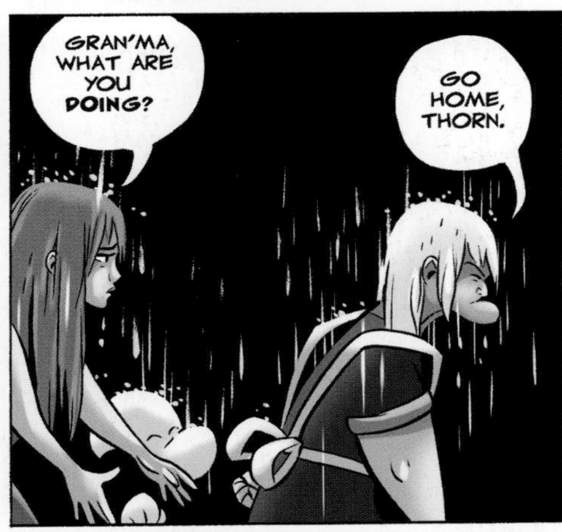
GRAN'MA, WHAT ARE YOU DOING?
GO HOME, THORN.

I'M NOT GOING BACK WITHOUT YOU!
AN' I'M NOT GOIN' BACK UNTIL YOU TELL US WHAT'S GOIN' ON!

HOW MUCH DID YOU **OVERHEAR** OF ME AN' THORN TALKIN' ABOUT OUR **DREAMS?**

KA-BOOM!

EVERYTHING . . .
I HEARD EVERY-THING.

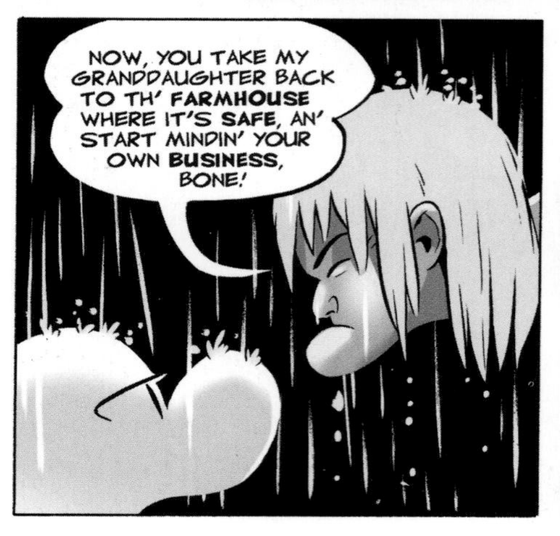
NOW, YOU TAKE MY GRANDDAUGHTER BACK TO TH' **FARMHOUSE** WHERE IT'S **SAFE**, AN' START MINDIN' YOUR OWN **BUSINESS**, BONE!

I'M NOT BEIN' **NOSEY! I'VE** BEEN HAVIN' WEIRD DREAMS, **TOO!** HOW COME YOU'RE **ACTIN'** LIKE THIS, GRAN'MA?

FIRST YOU COME SNEAKIN' INTO TH' BARN TO LISTEN IN ON OUR CONVERSATION, THEN YOU GO CHARGIN' OFF IN TH' WOODS LIKE A CRAZY PERSON!

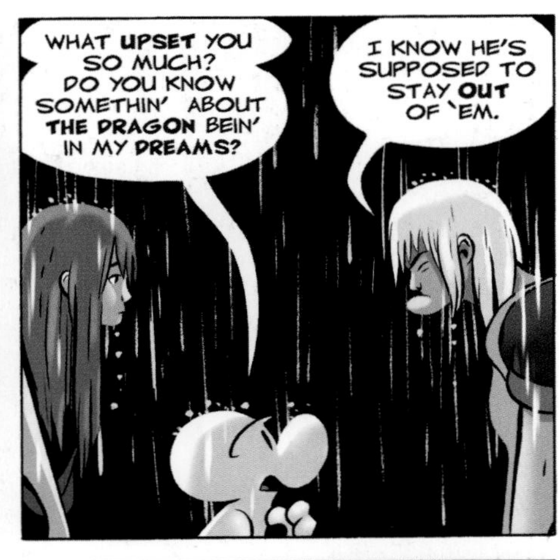
WHAT UPSET YOU SO MUCH? DO YOU KNOW SOMETHIN' ABOUT THE DRAGON BEIN' IN MY DREAMS?
I KNOW HE'S SUPPOSED TO STAY OUT OF 'EM.

WHAT?
GO BACK TO TH' HOUSE! THESE WOODS ARE DANGEROUS!

YOU'RE GOING TO SEE HIM RIGHT NOW, AREN'T YOU? YOU'RE GOING TO SEE THE DRAGON!
WHAT DO YOU MEAN HE'S SUPPOSED TO STAY OUT OF MY DREAMS?

FOR TH' LAST TIME, BONE, GET BACK TO TH' HOUSE BEFORE - -

KEERAAK BOOM!

DID YOU
SEE THAT?

I WASN'T
LOOKING!
Shh!

RAT CREATURES.
STAY LOW.

RUMMMMMBLE

ARE WE THERE YET?
NO.
JUST CHECKIN'.
WHOA, HOSS! YAH! EASY BOY!

WHOA! WHOA! GIDDIYUP!

YAH, MULE! YAH! YAH!

CIRCLE TH' WAGONS!!

WE'RE BLAZIN' A NEW TRAIL, BOYS!
IF HE GOES AROUND US ONE MORE TIME, I'M GONNA BLOW . . .

LET'S MAKE CAMP FOR TH' NIGHT! WE'LL SING SONGS, AN' EAT BEANS UNDER TH' STARS!

ARE WE THERE YET?
NO.
JUST CHECKIN'.
YEE-HAW!

DOUBLE OR NOTHING

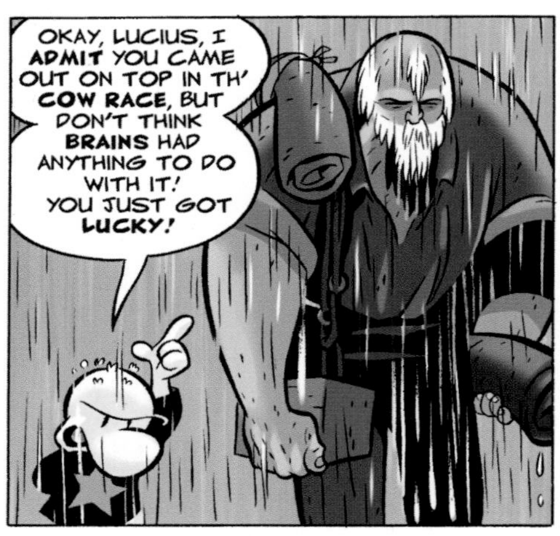
OKAY, LUCIUS, I ADMIT YOU CAME OUT ON TOP IN TH' COW RACE, BUT DON'T THINK BRAINS HAD ANYTHING TO DO WITH IT! YOU JUST GOT LUCKY!

I HAD YOU PEGGED FROM TH' VERY BEGINNING, SHORT STUFF. FACE IT, MY BRAIN WHIPPED YOUR BRAIN.

OH, YEAH? AND I SUPPOSE WE HAVE YOUR GENIUS TO THANK FOR THIS LITTLE STROLL THROUGH A MONSOON?
ARE YOU SAYIN' THIS IS MY FAULT?!

THIS TRIP SURE WASN'T MY IDEA! WE GOT ATTACKED BY RAT CREATURES, WE LOST OUR COWS, WE LOST OUR CART, AN' WE ALMOST GOT KILLED BECAUSE OF YOU!
!

WHY, YOU UNGRATEFUL, LITTLE RUNT! TH' ONLY REASON THE RAT CREATURES ATTACKED US WAS BECAUSE YOU WERE WITH US! I SAVED YOUR BUTT!

TECHNICALLY, I SAVED BOTH YOUR BUTTS!
GO RIDE YOUR HORSE!

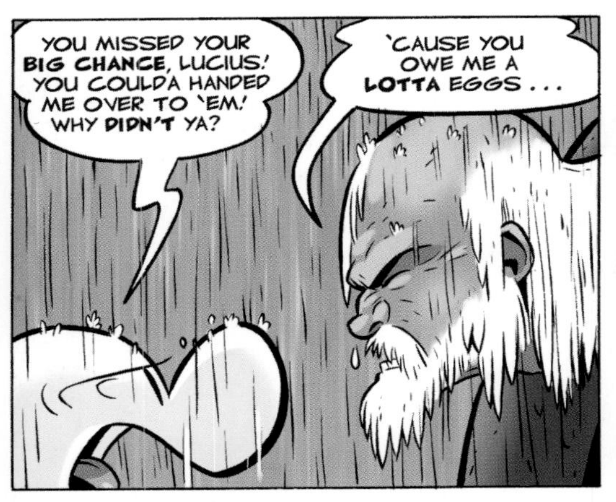
YOU MISSED YOUR BIG CHANCE, LUCIUS! YOU COULDA HANDED ME OVER TO 'EM! WHY DIDN'T YA?
'CAUSE YOU OWE ME A LOTTA EGGS . . .

. . . AND I'M REALLY LOOKIN' FORWARD TO BUSTIN' YOUR CHOPS ALL SUMMER LONG!

YOU'LL BE THANKIN' ME BY TH' END OF TH' SUMMER! AT LEAST WITH ME THERE, THAT TWO-BIT JOINT HAS A CHANCE TO TURN A PROFIT!
OH! OH!
NOW YOU GOT SOMETHIN' TO SAY ABOUT TH' WAY I RUN MY BAR?!

OH, PLEASE! DON'T EVEN GET ME STARTED!

YOU THINK YOU CAN RUN THE BARRELHAVEN TAVERN BETTER THAN I CAN?

YOU WOULDN'T KNOW A BOTTOM-LINE IF IT JUMPED UP AN' TUGGED YA ON TH' BEARD!
CARE TO MAKE A LITTLE WAGER ON THAT?

A WAGER? WHAT **KIND** OF WAGER?
I SAY MY CUSTOMERS **LIKE** TH' WAY I RUN MY PLACE!

WE'LL SPLIT TH' BAR RIGHT DOWN TH' **MIDDLE!** YOU TAKE ONE END, AND I'LL TAKE THE OTHER! WE'LL JUST **SEE** WHO TH' CUSTOMERS LIKE BETTER!

PIECE OF CAKE!
IS IT A **BET?**

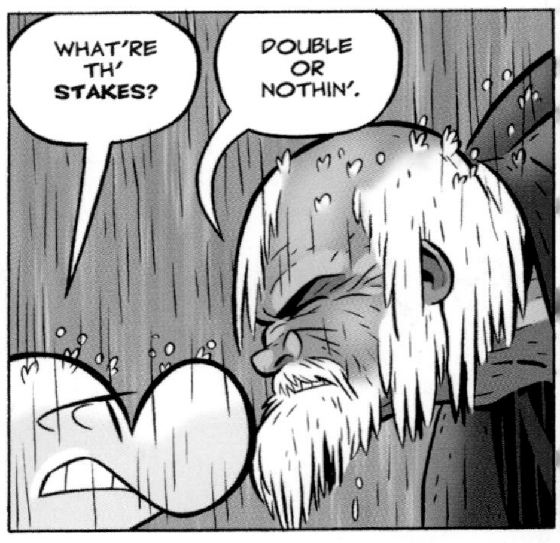
WHAT'RE TH' **STAKES?**
DOUBLE OR NOTHIN'.

AT TH' NEXT NEW MOON, IF **YOUR** END OF THE BAR IS MORE POPULAR, YOU'RE **OFF TH' HOOK!** IF **MY** END IS, YOU'RE GONNA BE WASHIN' DISHES FOR THE **REST OF YOUR LIFE!**

YOU'RE ON, PAL!
IT'S A BET, BUDDY!

I WAS WRONG. YOU DO KNOW HOW TO HAVE FUN!
RRRR.
RRRR.

RRRR.
RRRR.

SO. ARE WE THERE YET?
RRRR.
RRRR.
the Barrel Haven

HEY, EVERYBODY! LOOK! MR. DOWN IS BACK!

IT'S THOSE BONES!
TH' ONES THAT RIGGED TH' COW RACE!

LET'S GET 'EM!

HOLD IT RIGHT THERE!

WHAT DO YOU THINK YOU'RE DOIN'? ME AN' GRAN'MA BEN SETTLED ALL YOUR LOSSES! YOU GOT NO MORE BEEF WITH THESE BOYS!

BESIDES . . . THEY'RE MINE!

YOU GOT A LOT OF NERVE SHOWIN' YOUR FACE AROUND HERE AGAIN, BONE!
YEAH! YOU MUST HAVE SOME SORTA DEATH WISH!

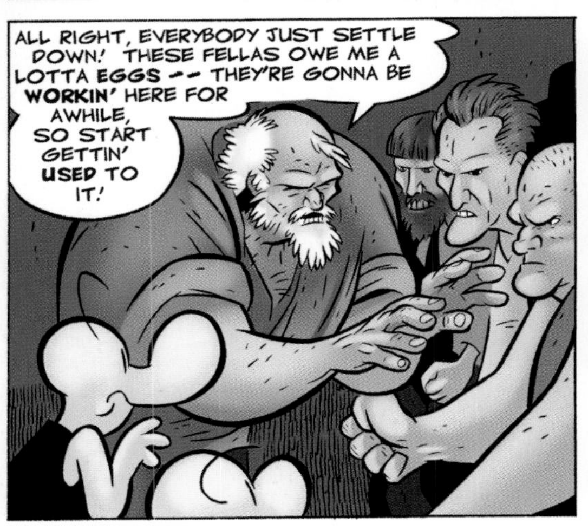
ALL RIGHT, EVERYBODY JUST SETTLE DOWN! THESE FELLAS OWE ME A LOTTA EGGS -- THEY'RE GONNA BE WORKIN' HERE FOR AWHILE, SO START GETTIN' USED TO IT!

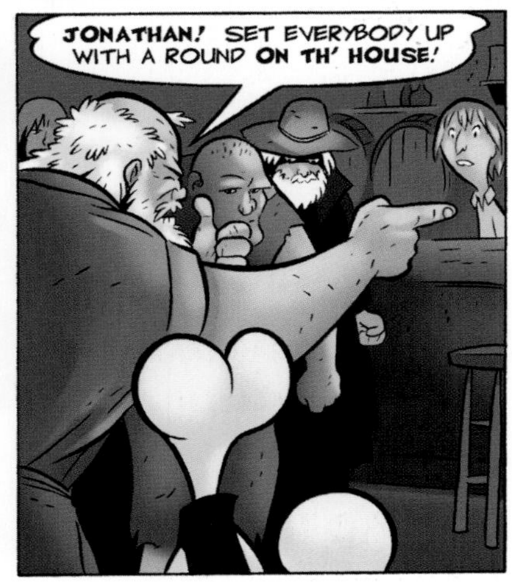
JONATHAN! SET EVERYBODY UP WITH A ROUND ON TH' HOUSE!

LOOKS LIKE YOU GOT YOUR WORK CUT OUT FOR YA IF YA WANNA BE TH' MOST POPULAR BARTENDER AROUND HERE, WOULDN'T YOU SAY SO, BONE?

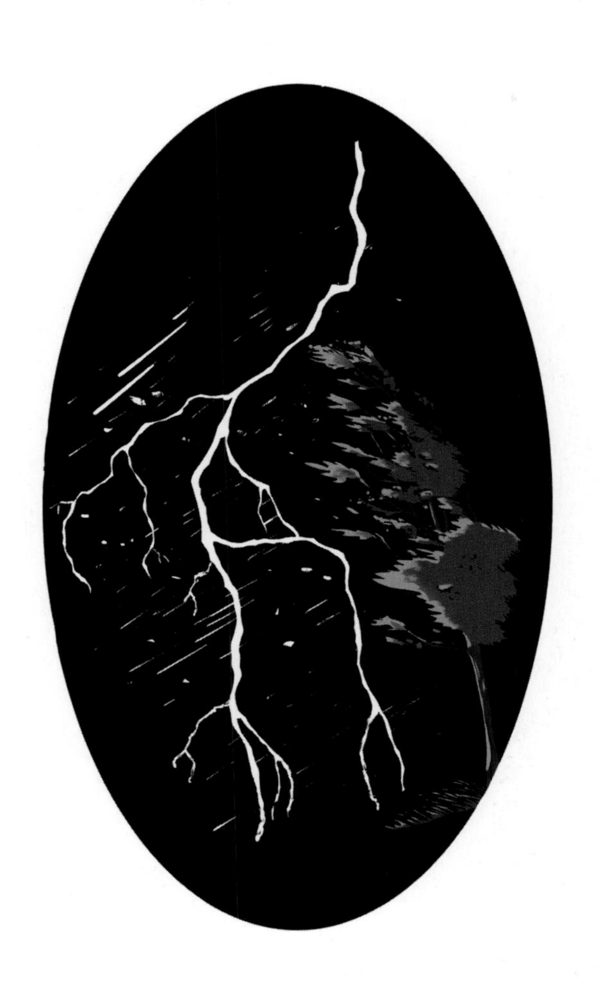

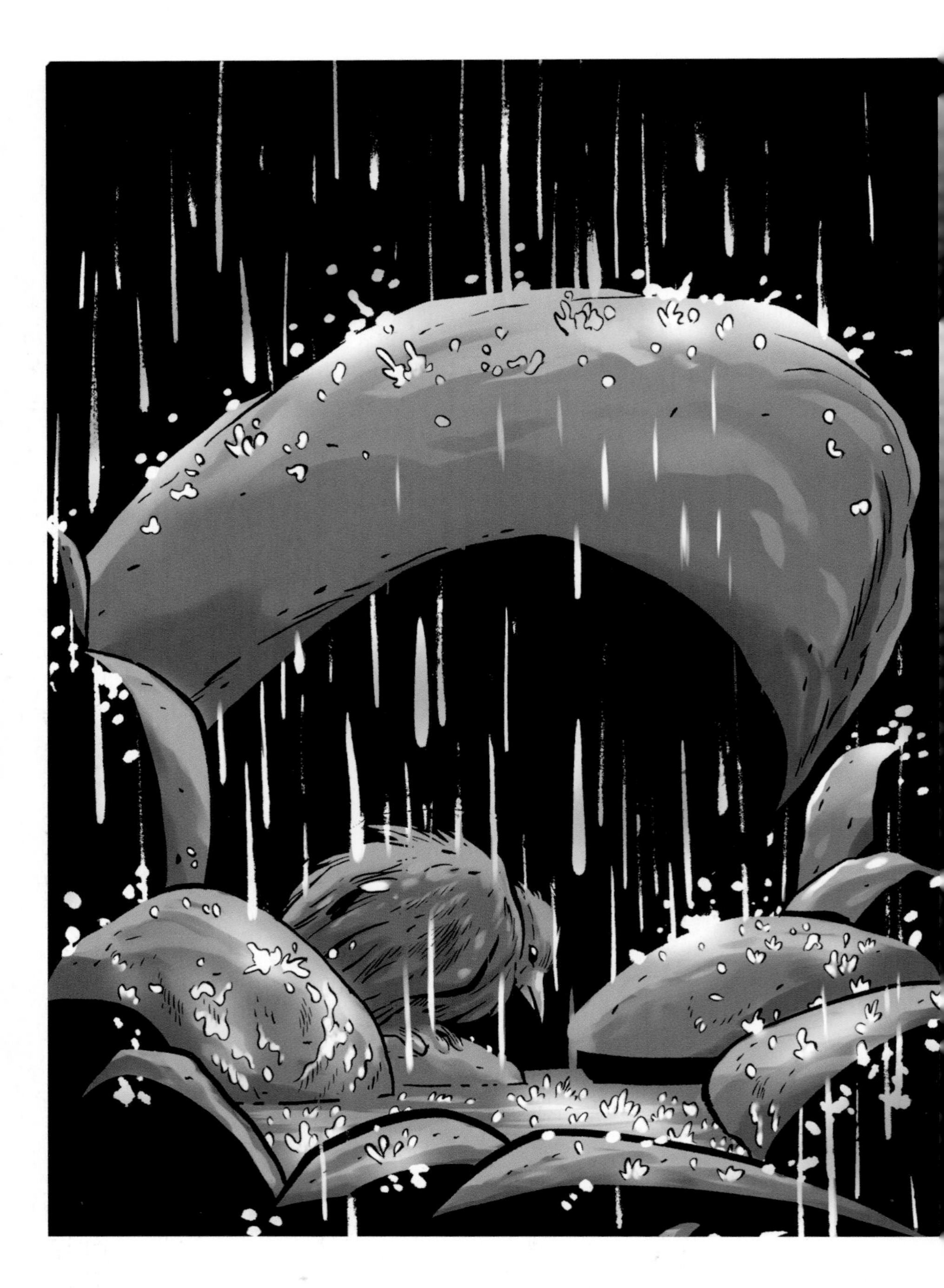

BONE

BOOM
KABABOOM

BONE. GET YOUR HEAD OVER BY THAT TREE AN' TAKE A LOOK AROUND.

GRAN'MA?

DO YOU THINK THE RAT CREATURES SAW US? MAYBE THEY DON'T KNOW WE'RE HERE.

THEY KNOW.
AN' IT WON'T BE LONG BEFORE THEY **FIND US**, EITHER.

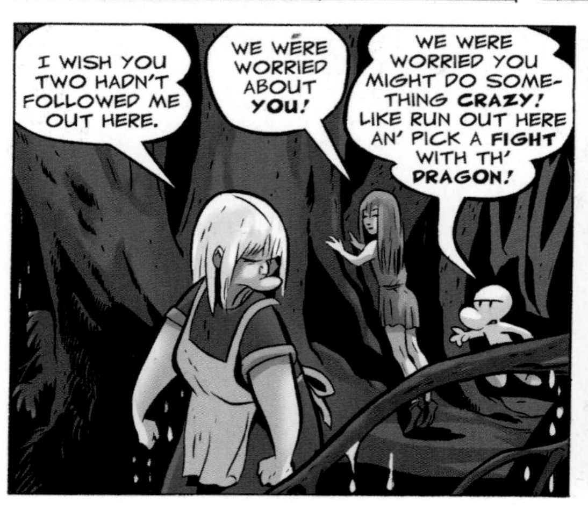
I WISH YOU TWO HADN'T FOLLOWED ME OUT HERE.
WE WERE WORRIED ABOUT **YOU**!
WE WERE WORRIED YOU MIGHT DO SOME-THING **CRAZY**! LIKE RUN OUT HERE AN' PICK A **FIGHT** WITH TH' **DRAGON**!

THAT'S ENOUGH!
WHY ARE YOU SO **MAD** AT HIM?

I DON'T WANNA HEAR ANOTHER WORD OUT OF YOU, BONE! THIS WHOLE THING IS YOUR FAULT!

GRAN'MA! THAT'S NOT TRUE!
KEEP STILL, THORN! EVERYTHING WAS UNDER CONTROL UNTIL HE CAME TO OUR VALLEY AND WOKE THE DRAGON!

YOU KNOW MORE ABOUT THE DRAGON THAN HE DOES!
WHAT I KNOW ABOUT TH' DRAGON IS MY --

HOLD IT.

GET DOWN.
GET DOWN. GET DOWN.

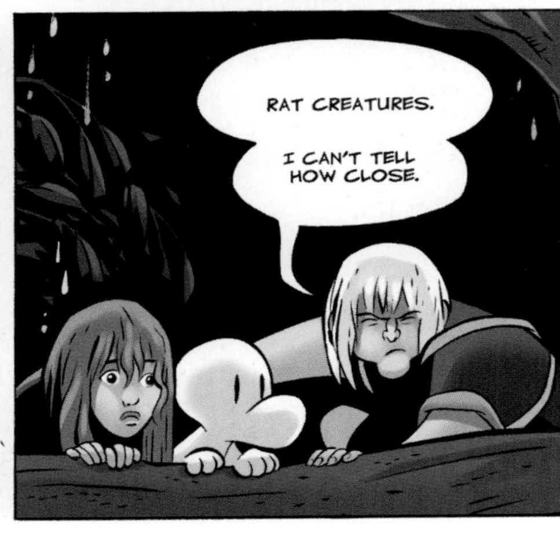
RAT CREATURES.
I CAN'T TELL HOW CLOSE.

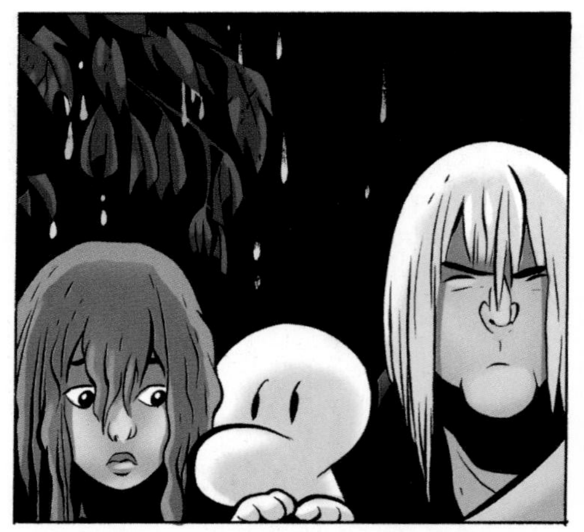

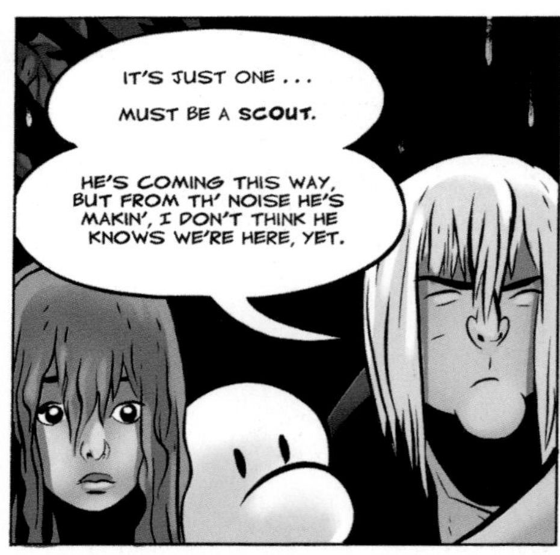
IT'S JUST ONE . . .
MUST BE A SCOUT.
HE'S COMING THIS WAY, BUT FROM TH' NOISE HE'S MAKIN', I DON'T THINK HE KNOWS WE'RE HERE, YET.

I'M GOIN' OUT THERE.
I WANT YOU TO SIT HERE AND NOT MOVE A MUSCLE! DO YOU UNDERSTAND ME?

DO YOU?!
YES.
UH, HUH.

OH, MAN.
THIS IS NOT GOOD.

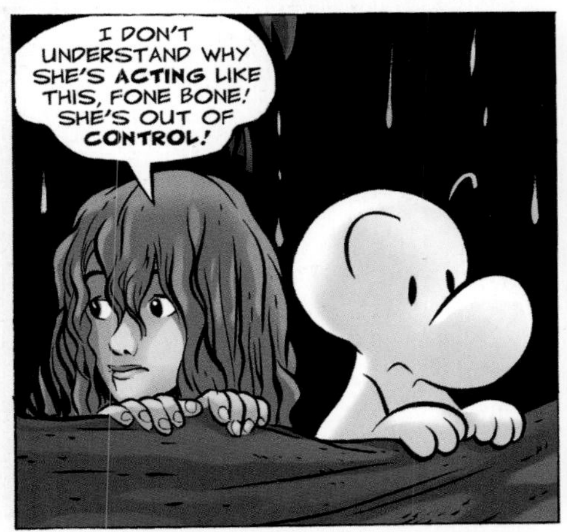
I DON'T UNDERSTAND WHY SHE'S ACTING LIKE THIS, FONE BONE! SHE'S OUT OF CONTROL!

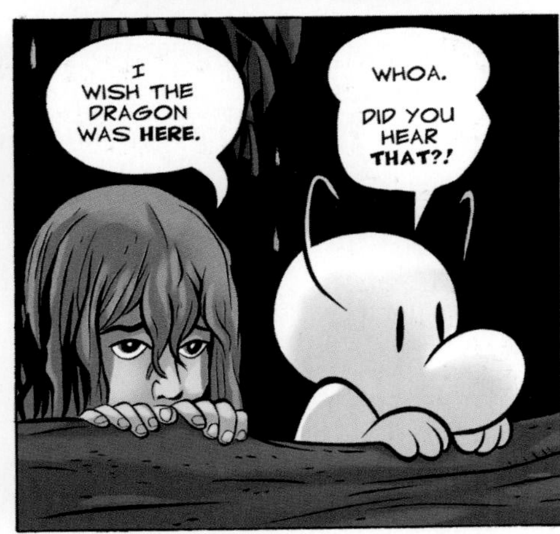
I WISH THE DRAGON WAS HERE.
WHOA.
DID YOU HEAR THAT?!

WHAT? I CAN'T HEAR ANYTHING EXCEPT THE RAIN --

KRACK
BOOM

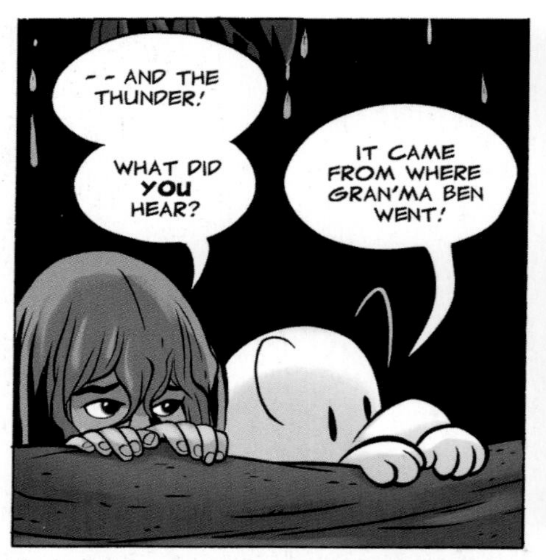
- - AND THE THUNDER!
WHAT DID YOU HEAR?
IT CAME FROM WHERE GRAN'MA BEN WENT!

IT - -
SOUNDED LIKE A SCREAM!

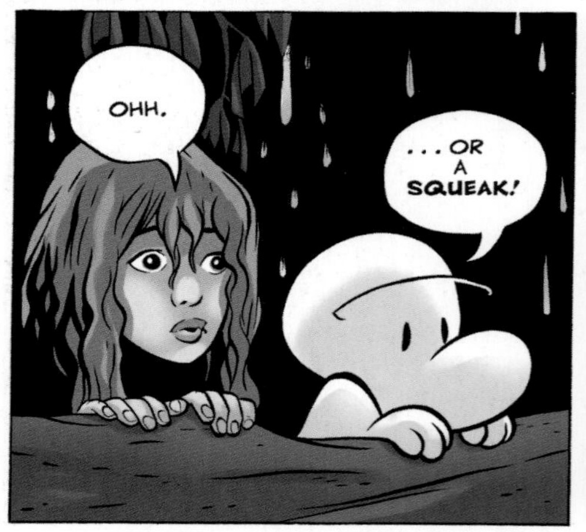
OHH.
. . . OR A SQUEAK!

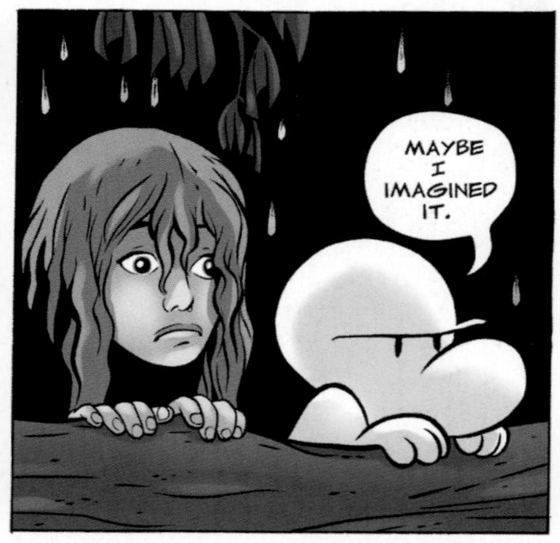
MAYBE I IMAGINED IT.

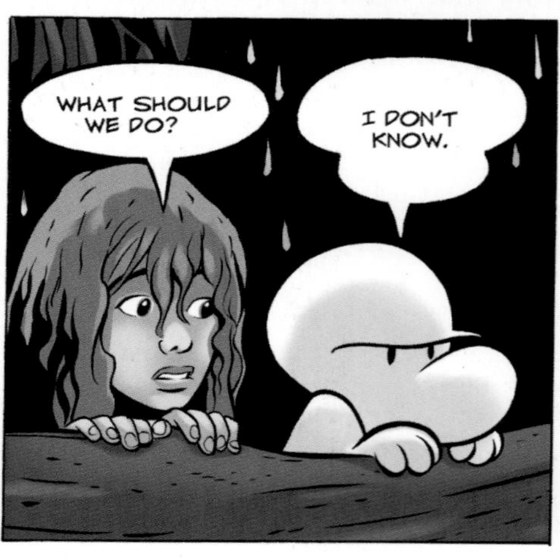
WHAT SHOULD WE DO?
I DON'T KNOW.

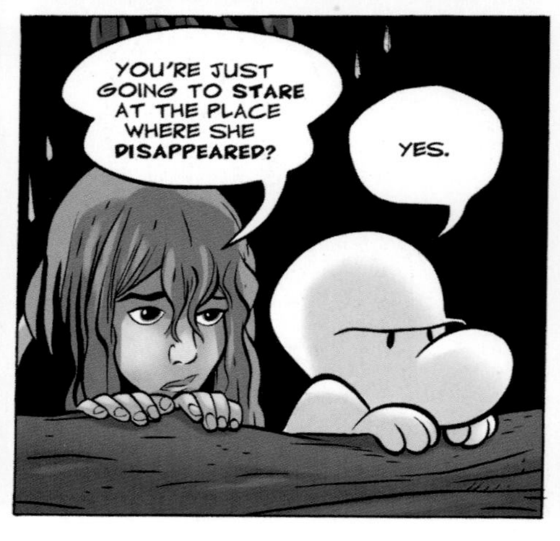
YOU'RE JUST GOING TO STARE AT THE PLACE WHERE SHE DISAPPEARED?
YES.

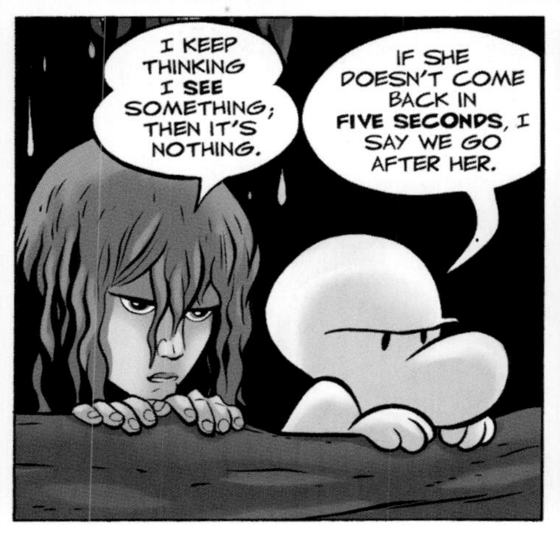
I KEEP THINKING I SEE SOMETHING; THEN IT'S NOTHING.
IF SHE DOESN'T COME BACK IN FIVE SECONDS, I SAY WE GO AFTER HER.

ONE -
TWO -
THREE -
FOUR -

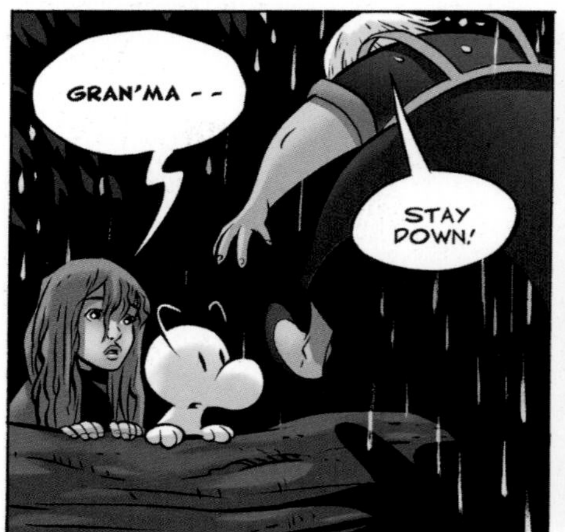
GRAN'MA - -
STAY DOWN!

IT'S BAD.
TH' FOREST IS SWARMING WITH RAT CREATURES. AND THEY'RE MOVIN' THIS WAY!

WE CAN'T STAY HERE AND WE CAN'T GET BACK TO TH' HOUSE . . .

WE'RE GONNA HAFTA OUTRUN 'EM.

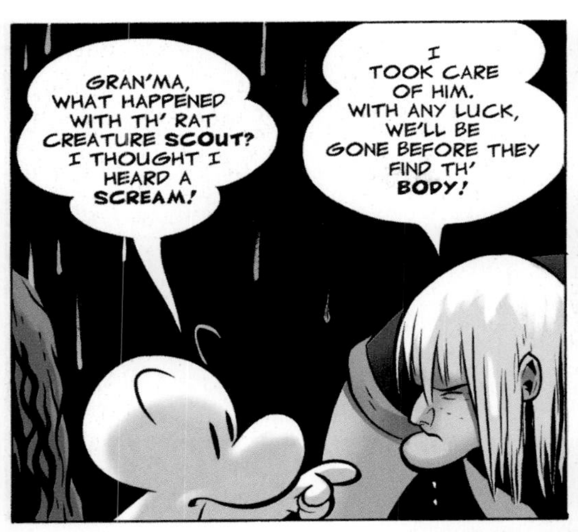
GRAN'MA, WHAT HAPPENED WITH TH' RAT CREATURE SCOUT? I THOUGHT I HEARD A SCREAM!
I TOOK CARE OF HIM. WITH ANY LUCK, WE'LL BE GONE BEFORE THEY FIND TH' BODY!

THE BODY?
YOU KILLED HIM?

WHERE DO YOU THINK YOU ARE? SAFE AT HOME IN BONEVILLE? IT'S ABOUT TIME YOU REALIZED THIS ISN'T A GAME, BONE!

LET'S GO.

I NEVER THOUGHT IT WAS A GAME.
SHE DIDN'T MEAN ANYTHING. SHE'S SCARED, TOO.
C'MON.

OHMYGOSH.
THORN! THEY SEE US!

HEY! LOOK OUT!!

SPLAT!

OHMYGOSH. OHMYGOSH.
HANG ON!

DRAGON! HELP US!

DRA-- MMMMF!

KEERAAKOW!

SNAP CRUNCH

KRACK!

THE DRAGON!
IT'S THE DRAGON!

HE CAME!
AN' HE CHASED OFF TH' RAT CREATURES!
WE'RE SAFE NOW!!

GET BEHIND TH' TREE.

KRACK KABOOM!

GRAN'MA! THE DRAGON JUST SAVED OUR LIVES! LEAVE HIM ALONE!

GRAN'MA?

PLEASE?

SIGH

KRAAAKKLE

I'M SO TIRED, BONE.

THANK YOU, GRAN'MA.

YOU THINK TH' DRAGON'LL BE THERE WHENEVER YOU NEED HIM . . .

. . . WELL, HE WON'T BE.

HE WASN'T ALWAYS THERE FOR ME.

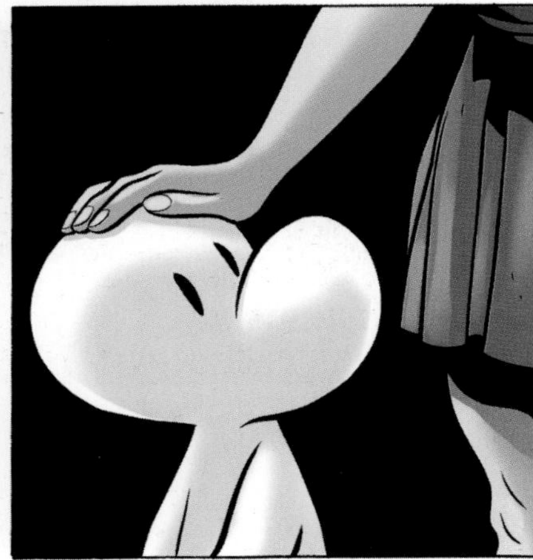

LET'S GO HOME.

AND WHEN WE GET THERE, TRY TO FIND YOUR **KNAPSACK**, OKAY?
I THINK IT'S TIME WE SHOWED GRAN'MA OUR **MAP**.

BONE
WHAT ARE THEY SAYING? I CANNOT HEAR THEM . . .
shh!

GRAN'MA BEN?
CAN WE TALK TO YOU?

TALK AWAY.
I CAN LISTEN AN' MEND FENCES AT TH' SAME TIME.

AREN'T THOSE FENCES KINDA SMALL FOR KEEPIN' OUT RAT CREATURES?
THESE ARE COW FENCES, BONE. BUT I'M FIXIN' 'EM TO LET THE MONSTERS KNOW WHERE TH' BOUNDARIES ARE!
CHUNK

GRAN'MA - -
JUST A MOMENT, THORN. THERE'S SOMETHIN' I HAVE TO SAY TO FONE BONE . . .

YOU SAVED OUR LIVES DURING THAT STORM YESTERDAY. IF YOU HADN'T CALLED OUT FOR TH' DRAGON TO COME AN' CHASE OFF THE RAT CREATURES, WE MIGHT NOT'VE MADE IT. AND, WELL . . . THIS ISN'T EASY FOR ME, BUT . . . I OWE YOU AN APOLOGY FOR TH' WAY I BEEN TREATIN' YOU.
!

OH, NO, GRAN'MA. YOU DON'T OWE ME ANYTHING . . .
YES, I **DO.** EVER SINCE YOU **CAME** TO OUR VALLEY, I'VE BEEN **SUSPICIOUS** OF YOU AN' YOUR COUSINS . . .

I'VE **BLAMED** YOU BOYS FOR ALL THE RAT CREATURE ATTACKS AN' EVERYTHING **ELSE** THAT'S GONE WRONG . . .

. . . AN' IN PARTICULAR, I BLAMED **YOU** FOR DISTURBING TH' **DRAGON.**

TRUTH **IS**, OUR TROUBLES HERE IN TH' **VALLEY** STARTED A LONG TIME BEFORE **YOU** GOT HERE.

APOLOGY ACCEPTED, GRAN'MA.

GRAN'MA . . . FONE BONE HAS SOMETHING IN HIS **KNAPSACK** THAT I WANT HIM TO SHOW YOU.

WE THINK YOU BETTER TAKE A LOOK AT THIS.

WHAT TH' HECK IS IT?
JUST READ IT.
UM . . . FONE BONE, THIS ISN'T THE - -

My heart beats for you, my pookie so true... I love you so MUCHer and MUCHess...

GIVE ME THAT!
....so say you'll be mine, my sweet Valentine! from the Duke of Pook to the Duchess.
YOU WANTED ME TO READ A LOVE POEM?

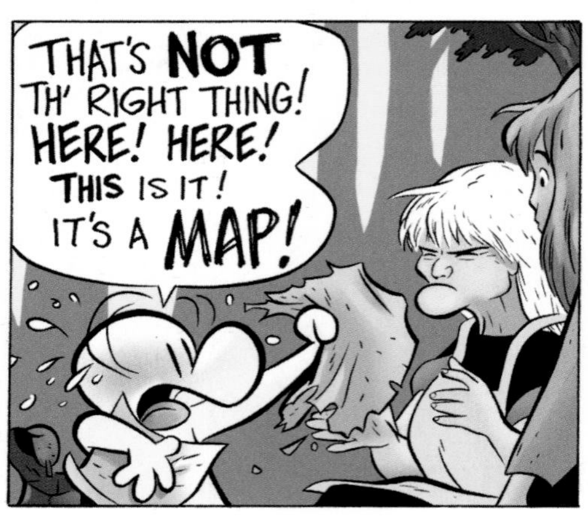
THAT'S NOT TH' RIGHT THING! HERE! HERE! THIS IS IT! IT'S A MAP!

JEEZ!

THIS IS A MAP?! IT'S SO FADED I CAN'T MAKE HEADS OR TAILS OUTTA THIS THING!

IT'S IN PRETTY BAD SHAPE. WE FOUND IT OUT IN TH' DESERT. LOOK! YOU CAN STILL MAKE OUT TH' MOUNTAINS AN' TH' WATERFALL! SEE? IT'S A MAP OF THIS VALLEY!

LOOKS LIKE IT WAS DRAWN BY A FIVE-YEAR-OLD!

IT WAS . . .

I DREW THAT MAP WHEN I WAS IN DEREN GARD WITH THE DRAGONS.

DON'T SAY ANOTHER WORD! THE FOREST HAS EARS!

INSIDE.
QUICKLY.

WELL?

WHERE DID YOU SAY YOU FOUND THAT **MAP?**
MY COUSINS AN' I FOUND IT AFTER WE GOT RUN OUTTA **BONEVILLE!**

WE WERE **LOST** OUT IN TH' **DESERT** AN' **SMILEY BONE** FOUND IT RIGHT BEFORE TH' **LOCUSTS** CAME AN' **SEPARATED** US!

LOCUSTS.
YES, MA'AM

WELL, NOW . . .
LOCUSTS. THAT'S - -
HMM. LET'S **THINK** ABOUT THIS . . .

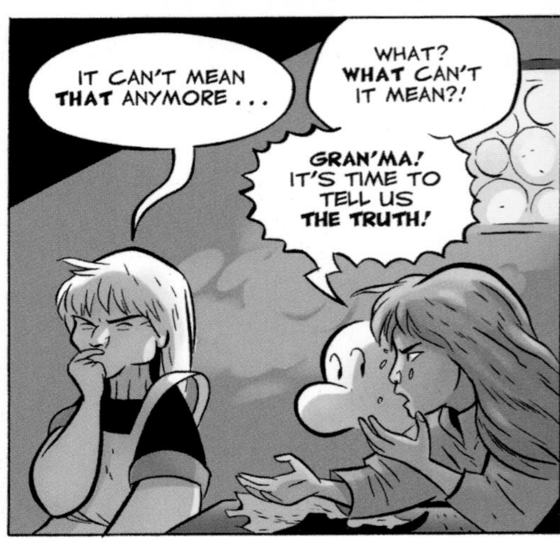
IT CAN'T MEAN **THAT** ANYMORE . . .
WHAT? **WHAT** CAN'T IT MEAN?!
GRAN'MA! IT'S TIME TO TELL US **THE TRUTH!**

FONE BONE . . .
BE A DEAR - -
RUN AND FETCH ME A DRINK OF WATER . . .
YES, MA'AM.

GRANDMOTHER, I'M WAITING.

YES.
YES, OF COURSE YOU ARE . . .

. . . IT'S JUST SO DIFFICULT TO KNOW WHERE TO START.

LET'S START WITH MY **DREAMS** . . .
YOU TOLD ME DRAGONS WERE **MAKE-BELIEVE**, BUT YOU **KNEW** THAT WASN'T TRUE!

the dragon's stair
Defen gard

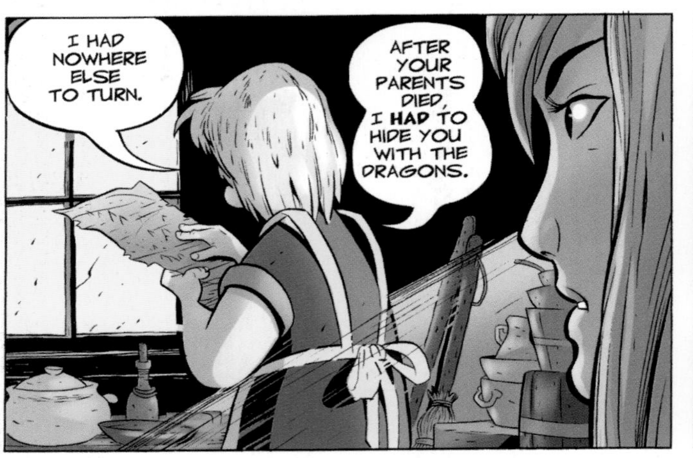
I HAD NOWHERE ELSE TO TURN.
AFTER YOUR PARENTS DIED, I **HAD** TO HIDE YOU WITH THE DRAGONS.

THE TWO OF US NEEDED TO DISAPPEAR.

THE DRAGONS KEPT YOU SAFE WHILE I SEARCHED FOR A SMALL TOWN WHERE NO ONE WOULD RECOGNIZE US.
WHY?

FOR YOUR SAFETY, CHILD.
WHY DID YOU **LIE** TO ME?!
WHY DID YOU TELL ME THAT IT NEVER **HAPPENED?!** THAT **DRAGONS** DON'T EVEN **EXIST?!!**

I WAS TRYING TO PROTECT YOU.
I WAS TRYING TO PROTECT THE **WHOLE VALLEY**.
I CAN'T BELIEVE THIS.

I HAD A LOT OF **RESPONSIBILITIES** IN THOSE DAYS.

YOU NEEDED TO BE **HIDDEN** SO IT WOULDN'T START ALL OVER AGAIN.
WHAT WERE YOU HIDING **FROM**?

DON'T RUSH ME, BONE. I'M NOT TOO FOND OF DISCUSSING **FAMILY MATTERS** AS IT IS.

IT STARTED BACK IN THE **BIG WAR** . . .

WE WERE FIGHTING THE RAT CREATURES OVER WHO OWNED THE VALLEY.
WE HAD IT AND THEY **WANTED** IT.

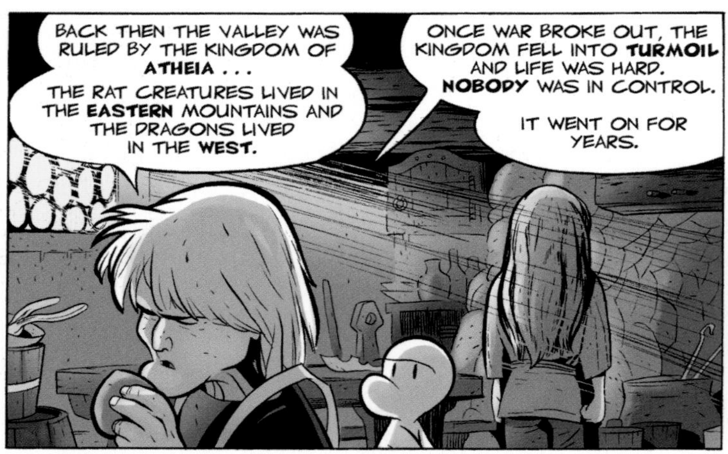
BACK THEN THE VALLEY WAS RULED BY THE KINGDOM OF ATHEIA . . .
THE RAT CREATURES LIVED IN THE EASTERN MOUNTAINS AND THE DRAGONS LIVED IN THE WEST.
ONCE WAR BROKE OUT, THE KINGDOM FELL INTO TURMOIL AND LIFE WAS HARD. NOBODY WAS IN CONTROL.
IT WENT ON FOR YEARS.

FAMILIES FELL APART AND WE ALL LOST FRIENDS.

THEN ONE DAY, THE WAR WAS OVER. THE RAT CREATURES WITHDREW AND DISAPPEARED INTO THE MOUNTAINS.

WE KNEW THEY'D BE BACK - - BUT WHEN THEY DID COME BACK, SOMETHING HAD CHANGED. THEIR NEW ATTACKS WERE MUCH MORE VICIOUS.
ATTACKS SO FAST AND BRUTAL THEY BECAME KNOWN AS THE NIGHTS OF LIGHTNING.

I WAS UP HERE IN THE NORTH, TRYING TO WORK AN ALLIANCE BETWEEN DRAGONS AND MEN, WHEN I HEARD THE NEWS . . .
ATHEIA HAD FALLEN AND ALL OF THE ROYAL FAMILY HAD BEEN KILLED.

SLOWLY, WITH THE HELP OF THE DRAGONS, WE FORCED THE RATS OUT OF THE VALLEY AND A TREATY WAS SIGNED . . . THE RATS AGREED TO STAY IN THE MOUNTAINS, AND THE VALLEY PEOPLE AGREED NOT TO REBUILD THE KINGDOM.
OKAY, BUT WHY DID YOU HAVE TO HIDE THORN?

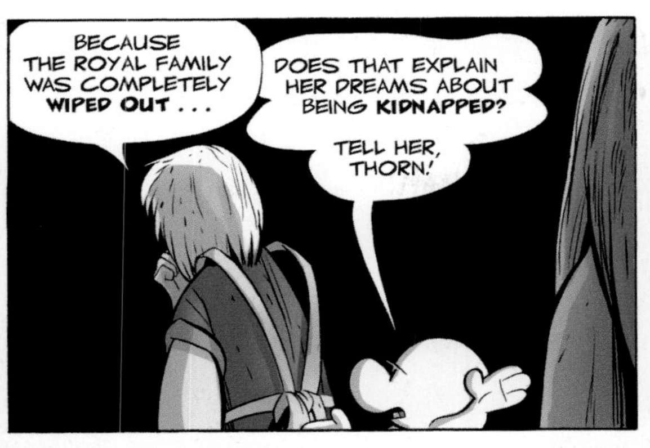
BECAUSE THE ROYAL FAMILY WAS COMPLETELY **WIPED OUT** . . .
DOES THAT EXPLAIN HER DREAMS ABOUT BEING **KIDNAPPED?**
TELL HER, THORN!

IN ONE OF MY DREAMS - - - I AM TAKEN OVER THE MOUNTAINS AT NIGHT BY PEOPLE WHOSE FACES I CANNOT **SEE** . . .

. . . THEY HAVE **HOODS** PULLED DOWN OVER THEIR FACES.
GRAN'MA, I THINK ONE OF THEM IS **YOU.**

THEN, SOMEWHERE **HIGH** IN THE MOUNTAINS, WE ARE **BETRAYED!**

THE OTHERS ARE ATTACKED BY RAT CREATURES, BUT YOU GO ON ALONE AND HAND ME OVER TO THE **DRAGONS - - YOURSELF!**

I THINK YOU SHOULD SIT DOWN.

THE OTHER HOODED FIGURES IN YOUR DREAM WERE YOUR PARENTS ... AND THEY DIED THAT NIGHT ON THE MOUNTAIN PASS. ATHEIA WAS BURNING AND THEY, ALONG WITH A NURSEMAID, MANAGED TO SNEAK YOU OUT OF THE CITY.

GO ON.

TRAVELING ONLY AT NIGHT, AND IN COMPLETE SECRECY, THEY MANAGED TO MAKE THEIR WAY NORTH ALONG THE FOOTHILLS OF THE MOUNTAINS TO THE PASS CALLED THE DRAGON'S STAIR.

I MET THE ROYAL PARTY THERE ON THE PASS ...
I WAS ESCORTING THEM TO THE DRAGONS' STRONGHOLD IN DEREN GARD WHEN WE WERE BETRAYED!

A BAND OF RAT CREATURES LED BY THEIR CHIEFTAIN KINGDOK APPEARED IN THE PASS BEHIND US. YOUR PARENTS CHOSE TO STAY AND FIGHT THE MONSTERS WHILE I WENT ON TO DELIVER YOU TO THE GREAT RED DRAGON.

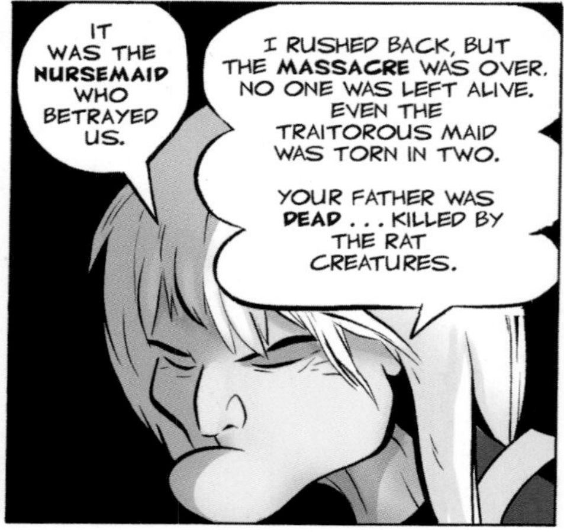
IT WAS THE NURSEMAID WHO BETRAYED US.
I RUSHED BACK, BUT THE MASSACRE WAS OVER. NO ONE WAS LEFT ALIVE. EVEN THE TRAITOROUS MAID WAS TORN IN TWO.
YOUR FATHER WAS DEAD ... KILLED BY THE RAT CREATURES.

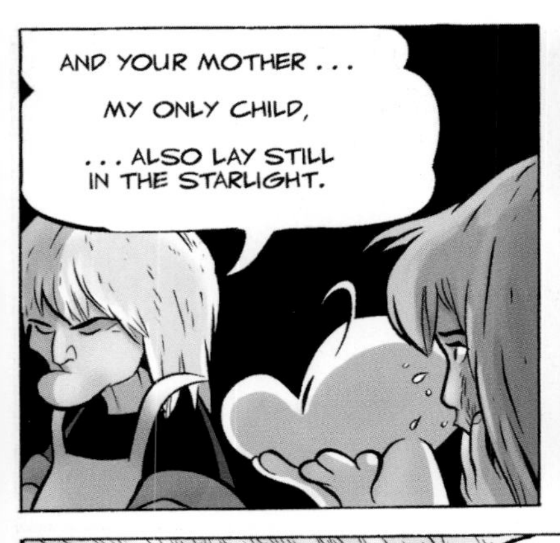
AND YOUR MOTHER . . .
MY ONLY CHILD,
. . . ALSO LAY STILL IN THE STARLIGHT.

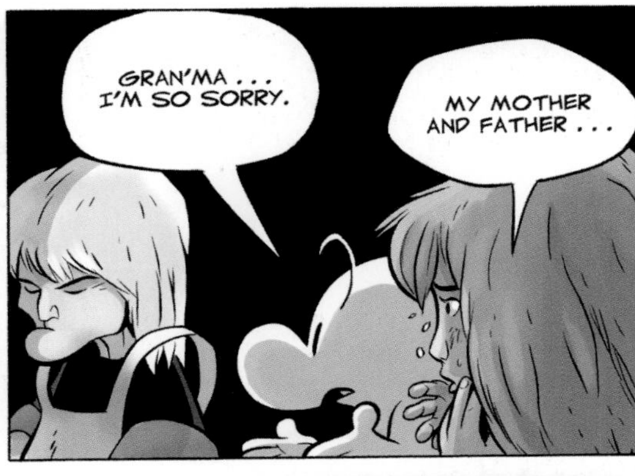
GRAN'MA . . . I'M SO SORRY.
MY MOTHER AND FATHER . . .

YOUR MOTHER AND FATHER WERE **KING** AND **QUEEN** OF **ATHEIA.** AND I WAS **QUEEN** OF THE LAND BEFORE THEM.
AND YOU, **THORN HARVESTAR**, ARE HEIR TO THE THRONE, AND I WILL **NOT** LET ANYTHING HAPPEN TO YOU!

I THOUGHT WE COULD KEEP YOU SAFE. LIVE OUT OUR DAYS HERE . . . RAISING THE COWS, FARMING A LITTLE PLOT OF LAND.

BUT IF THE LOCUSTS ARE BACK, THEN WAR IS UNAVOIDABLE . . .

. . . AND I HAVE FAILED.

...MASTER...

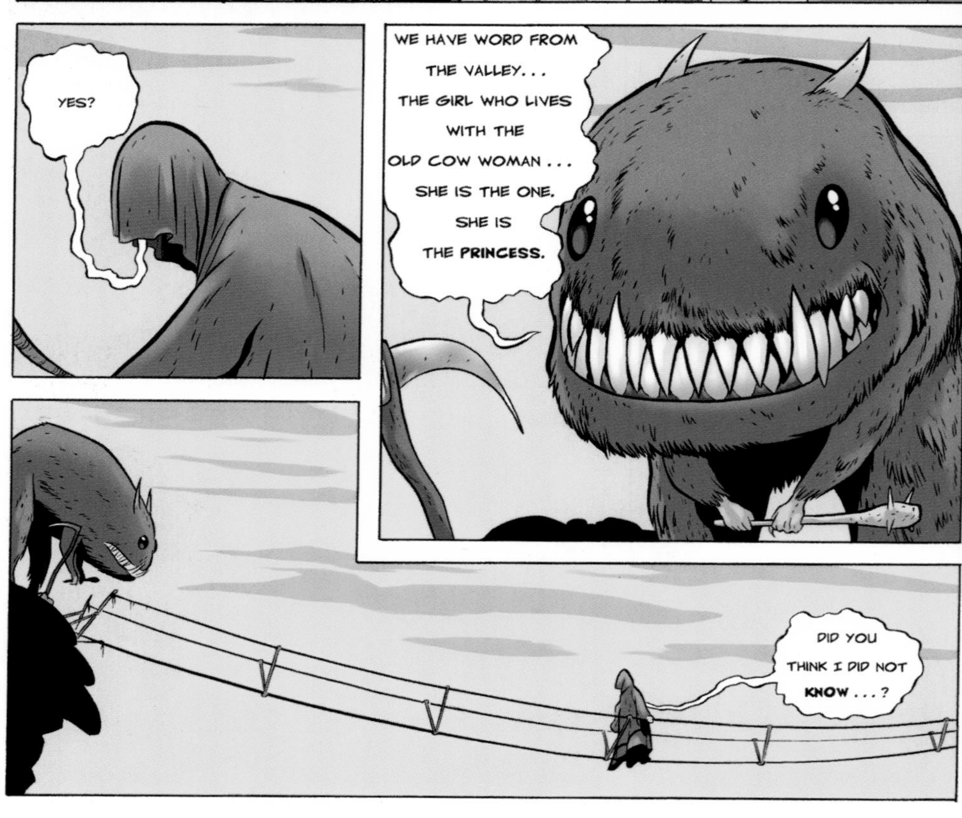
YES?
WE HAVE WORD FROM THE VALLEY... THE GIRL WHO LIVES WITH THE OLD COW WOMAN... SHE IS THE ONE. SHE IS THE PRINCESS.
DID YOU THINK I DID NOT KNOW...?

. . . MASTER?

. . . IF I WAITED . . .
FOR YOUR COWARDLY UNDERLINGS TO BRING ME INFORMATION . . . . . WE WOULD ALL GROW OLD LISTENING TO SILENCE . . . . .

I SUSPECT THAT IF YOU, KINGDOK . . . SHOWED LESS FEAR FOR THE RED DRAGON . . . YOUR WARRIORS MIGHT FOLLOW YOUR EXAMPLE . . .

NOW LEAVE ME . . .

WHAT NEWS DO YOU BRING US?

WE HAVE OUR ARMY.
THE POPULATION OF THE CAMP IS NEARING TEN THOUSAND . . . MORE RECRUITS ARRIVE EACH MORNING . . .
THAT IS GOOD.

THERE IS SOMETHING ELSE YOU WISH TO ASK US ABOUT?

THE GIRL . . . HER DREAMS ARE LIKE A BEACON . . . AND YET I CANNOT **REACH** HER . . .
IS HER STRENGTH SO GREAT?

EVEN IN HER IGNORANCE, HER STRENGTH IS GREAT . . . BUT THERE IS SOMETHING MORE . . . AS I REACHED OUT TO HER . . . A **NEW** BEACON APPEARED . . .
THE RED DRAGON SEEKS TO BRING A PAWN INTO PLAY. DO NOT CONCERN YOURSELF.
WHAT NEWS DO YOU BRING US OF THE STAR-BEARER?

THE ONE WHO BEARS A STAR IS AGAIN WITH THE VILLAGERS . . . IF IT IS YOUR DESIRE . . . WE WILL ATTACK THE TOWN.
AWAIT OUR INSTRUCTIONS.

MY LORD . . . THE RED DRAGON IS DANGEROUS. SHOULD WE NOT PREPARE - -
ASK NO MORE QUESTIONS.

......BUT WHAT OF THIS NEW LIGHT IN THE DREAMING......?
DO WE NOT.... IGNORE THIS AT OUR PERIL?

BONE
The Barrel Haven
L. Down. Prop.
EVERYBODY GATHER 'ROUND! I GOT A LITTLE ANNOUNCEMENT TO MAKE!
THAT MEANS YOU, WENDELL!
AN' YOU, TOO, EUCLID!
ALL RIGHT NOW, LISTEN UP! I'M GONNA TELL YA ABOUT A CONTEST!
BUT FIRST . . .

I KNOW HOW YOU FELLAS FEEL ABOUT THESE BONE BOYS . . .

. . . YOU WANNA KILL 'EM FOR MESSIN' WITH TH' COW RACE!

RRR!
GRR!
RRR!
GRR!
RRRR!
RRR!
WELL, SO DO I, BUT THEY OWE ME A LOTTA EGGS, AN' SO THEY GOTTA STAY RIGHT HERE AN' WORK IT OFF!

THAT MEANS I DON'T WANT NO TROUBLE FROM YOU GUYS. YOU GOT ME?
WHY NOT, LUCIUS? THEY GOTTA PAY FOR WHAT THEY DID!
I SAY WE TEAR THEIR LEGS OFF!

YEAH!
THEY TRIED TO MAKE FOOLS OUTTA US!
YOU MADE FOOLS OUTTA YERSELVES!

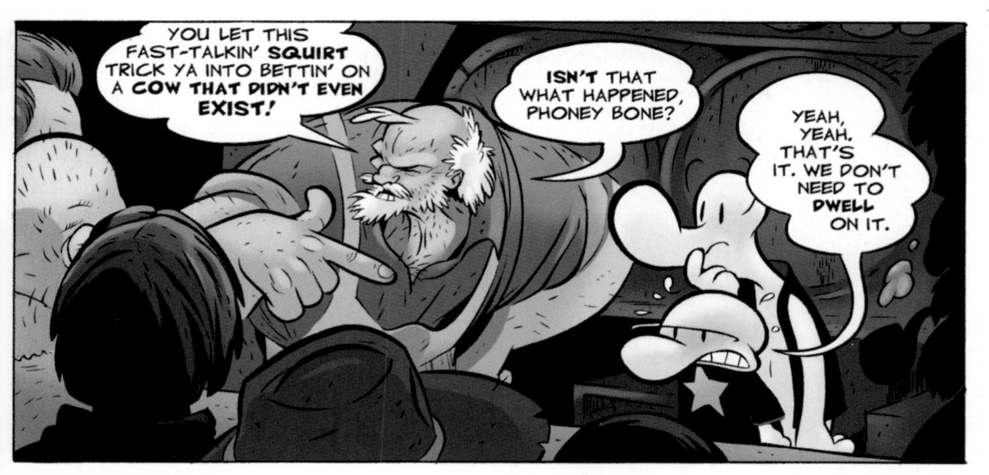
YOU LET THIS FAST-TALKIN' SQUIRT TRICK YA INTO BETTIN' ON A COW THAT DIDN'T EVEN EXIST!
ISN'T THAT WHAT HAPPENED, PHONEY BONE?
YEAH, YEAH. THAT'S IT. WE DON'T NEED TO DWELL ON IT.

YOU LET YERSELVES BE TALKED INTO BETTIN' YER LIFE'S SAVINGS ON THIS IDIOT DRESSED IN A COW SUIT!
IS IT ME, OR IS IT GETTING STUFFY IN HERE?

BUT I WARNED YA! I TOLD YA YOU WERE BEIN' PLAYED FOR A BUNCHA SAPS, BUT YA DIDN'T LISTEN TO ME, DIDJA? HUH? DIDJA?

THAT'S RIGHT! AN' WHEN GRAN'MA BEN WON THAT RACE, I WAS TH' ONLY ONE WHO BET ON HER! ME AN' GRAN'MA COULDA SPLIT THAT POT, BUT NOOOOO . . . .
WE FELT SORRY FOR YA!

ALL BETS WERE OFF, AN' WE LET YA HAVE YER LIVESTOCK BACK! ALL TOLD, I'D SAY YOU GIRLS GOT OFF PRETTY EASY!

GRR!
RR!
OKAY, NOW THAT THAT'S SETTLED, I WANNA TELL YA ABOUT THIS LITTLE CONTEST WE'RE GONNA HAVE . . .
RRR!
. . . THESE TWO - -

KILL`EM!
!
RIP THEIR HEADS OFF!

BACK OFF OR I START SWINGIN'!

HERE'S TH' DEAL, SEE? AS LONG AS PHONEY BONE AN' HIS COUSIN SMILEY BONE ARE WORKIN' HERE, NOBODY LAYS A FINGER ON 'EM OR THEY ANSWER TO ME! CLEAR?!

CLEAR.
ALL RIGHT THEN.

... NOW, THIS CONTEST I WAS TELLIN' YOU ABOUT - - IT'S BETWEEN ME AN' MISTER PHONEY BONE HERE. HE THINKS HE CAN RUN THIS JOINT BETTER THAN I CAN! WE'RE GONNA LET YOU DECIDE!

FROM NOW ON, THIS BAR WILL BE DIVIDED IN TWO! I'LL RUN THIS END, AN' TH' BONES'LL RUN THAT END.

HERE'S TH' RULES: YOU CAN TAKE YER BUSINESS TO WHICHEVER END OF TH' BAR YOU WANT! AFTER ONE MOON, THE END THAT EARNS TH' MOST EGGS FOR TH' TAVERN WINS!!

YOU CAN EITHER VOTE FOR ME, OR YOU CAN VOTE FOR PHONEY!
EVERYBODY UNDERSTAND TH' RULES?
GOOD!

WHO WANTS A DRINK?

WHAT ARE WE GONNA DO, PHONEY? NOBODY'S GONNA ORDER ANYTHING FROM US! IF WE LOSE THIS CONTEST WE'RE GONNA BE WASHIIN' DISHES FOR TH' REST OF OUR LIVES!

I KNOW, I KNOW. THIS WASN'T ONE OF TH' SMARTEST BETS I'VE EVER MADE.
BUT WE'LL THINK OF SOMETHIN', RIGHT? WE ALWAYS DO!

SURE! ALL WE GOTTA DO IS COME UP WITH SOME WAY TO LURE TH' TOWNSPEOPLE BACK DOWN TO OUR END. HOW HARD CAN THAT BE?
RIGHT! I'M ON IT! WE'LL HOLD A LECTURE SERIES! NO, WAIT! WE'LL USE PUPPETS! REALLY CUTE PUPPETS WITH HIGH, SQUEAKY VOICES!

GROAN
WE'RE DEAD.

GRAN'MA BEN?

THORN --
. . . UM . . . I MEAN, PRINCESS --
DON'T CALL ME THAT.

SORRY.

ALL THOSE DREAMS . . . THEY WERE REAL.

THOSE DREAMS WERE MEMORIES OF THINGS THAT REALLY HAPPENED TO ME.

SOMETHING LIKE THAT.
THEY WERE JUST LIKE YOU SAID...

IN MY DREAMS I WAS TAKEN OUT OF A BURNING PALACE AS A LITTLE GIRL...

...AND IN THE DARK OF NIGHT, I WAS BROUGHT OVER THE MOUNTAINS TO THE DRAGONS' CAVE...

I EVEN DREAMED ABOUT THE AMBUSH ON THE DRAGON'S STAIR! I DREAMED ABOUT THE MURDER OF MY PARENTS AND I DIDN'T EVEN KNOW IT!
HOW CAN THIS BE?! HOW CAN I DREAM ABOUT THINGS THAT HAPPENED TO ME, BUT NOT REMEMBER THEM HAPPENING?!

SOMETIMES DREAMS KNOW MORE THAN WE DO.

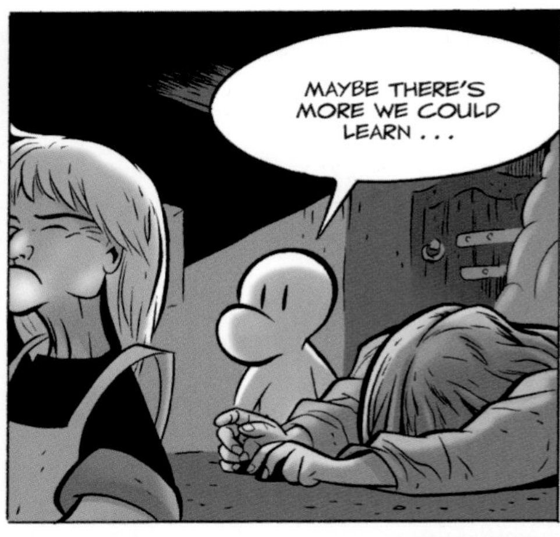
MAYBE THERE'S MORE WE COULD LEARN . . .

THORN, WHAT HAPPENS IN YOUR DREAM AFTER YOU GET TO THE DRAGONS' CAVE?

THE DRAGONS TAKE ME ON A LONG, LONG JOURNEY . . . UNDERGROUND
WE GO TO A SPECIAL CHAMBER. IT'S VERY DARK AT FIRST . . .

. . . BUT THEN MY EYES GET USED TO THE BLACKNESS . . . I'M AWARE OF SHAPES IN THE CAVE AROUND ME . . .

. . . I CAN SEE NOW . . . THERE IS LIGHT . . . I AM IN A HUGE CAVERN . . . SURROUNDED BY DRAGONS. DOZENS OF THEM. AND WE'RE ALL LOOKING AT SOMETHING . . .

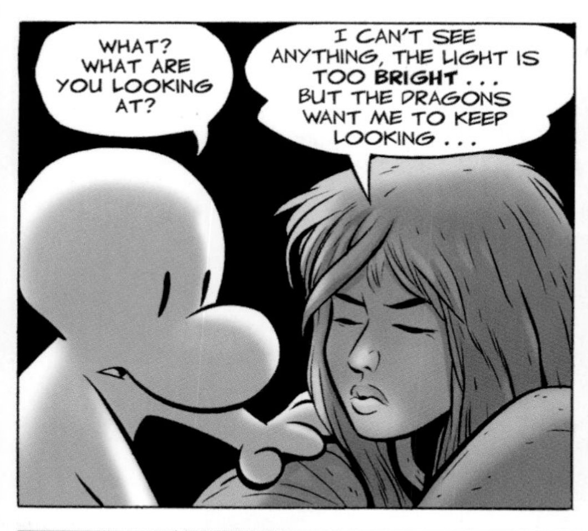
WHAT? WHAT ARE YOU LOOKING AT?
I CAN'T SEE ANYTHING, THE LIGHT IS TOO **BRIGHT** . . . BUT THE DRAGONS WANT ME TO KEEP LOOKING . . .

I THINK THE DRAGONS SEE SOMETHING, BUT I DON'T. IT'S TOO BRIGHT.

WHAT ELSE?
AFTER THAT I STAYED WITH THE DRAGONS. BUT I NEVER SAW THAT CHAMBER AGAIN . . .

WHAT ABOUT THE **GARDEN?** DON'T YOU WANT TO TELL GRAN'MA BEN ABOUT **THAT?**

SHE HEARD IT. SHE WAS **LISTENING IN** ON OUR CONVERSATION OUT IN THE **BARN.**

YES, I HEARD YOU.

I CAN'T BELIEVE IT . . . ALL THESE YEARS OF HIDING FOR **NOTHING.**

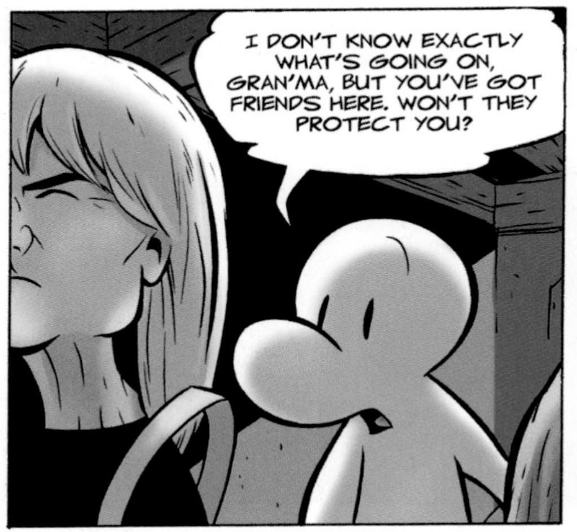
I DON'T KNOW EXACTLY WHAT'S GOING ON, GRAN'MA, BUT YOU'VE GOT FRIENDS HERE. WON'T THEY PROTECT YOU?

WE'RE NOT TALKING ABOUT FIGHTING OFF A BUNCH OF RAT CREATURES, BONE! THIS IS THE **LORD OF THE LOCUST!**

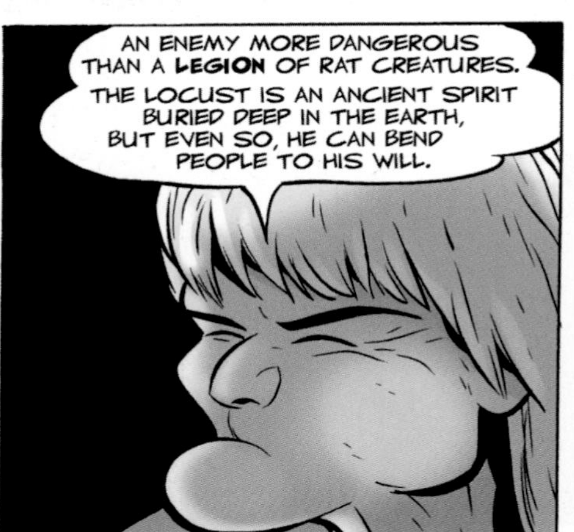
AN ENEMY MORE DANGEROUS THAN A **LEGION** OF RAT CREATURES. THE LOCUST IS AN ANCIENT SPIRIT BURIED DEEP IN THE EARTH, BUT EVEN SO, HE CAN BEND PEOPLE TO HIS WILL.

AND YOU'RE **SURE** IT WAS THE DRAGON IN **YOUR** DREAM, RIGHT?
I **GUESS** SO, BUT I STILL DON'T UNDERSTAND - -

MMMM.
HE'S DOING THIS ON **PURPOSE!**
WHAT?
WHAT'S HE DOING?
BEING IN MY DREAM? I DON'T GET IT.

C'MON, GRAN'MA! WE HAVE A RIGHT TO KNOW!
THERE'S STILL SOMETHING YOU'RE NOT TELLING US!

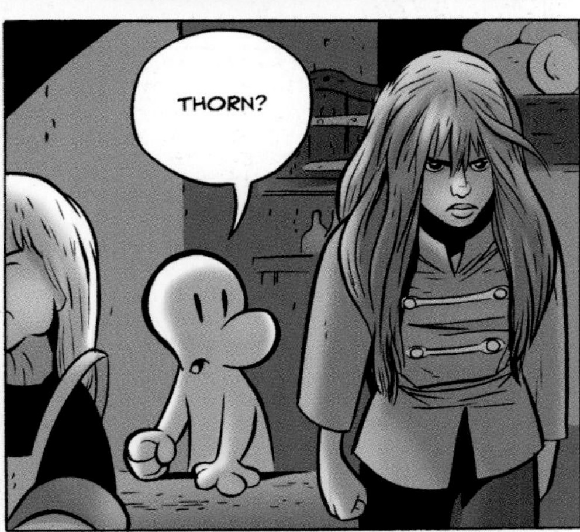
THORN?

SLAM!

THORN!

HEY!

WAIT UP.

YOU FEEL OKAY?
I DON'T FEEL ANYTHING.

DO YOU WANT ME TO LEAVE YOU ALONE?

OKAY. I'LL GO.

I'M SORRY.
LISTEN. IF YOU NEED ANYTHING, JUST . . . UH . . . JUST TELL ME, ALL RIGHT?

HEY, EVERYBODY! COME OVER HERE AN' TRY SOME BEER!

RRRR.
I KNEW PUPPETS WOULDN'T WORK.

WELL, THAT'S IT! WE'RE BEATEN! NOBODY WANTS ANYTHING FROM US! READY TO THROW IN TH' TOWEL, CUZ?

ARE YOU CRAZY? THAT GORILLA CAN'T BEAT ME! ESPECIALLY WHEN IT COMES TO TURNIN' A PROFIT!

YOU KEEP TRYIN' TO THINK OF SOMETHIN'! I'M GONNA GO DOWN AN' TAKE A LOOK AT WHAT HE'S DOIN'.
I'M PUTTIN' ON MY THINKIN' CAP!

WELL, WELL, WELL, WELL . . . LOOK WHAT SLITHERED UP! READY TO CALL IT QUITS, SMART-GUY?
I ADMIT THIS MIGHT BE A LITTLE TOUGHER THAN I THOUGHT.

YOU'RE WELCOME TO HANG AROUND THIS END. YOU MIGHT LEARN SOMETHIN' ABOUT RUNNIN' A BUSINESS HERE ON TH' WINNING END OF TH' BAR!
DON'T GET SMUG! IT AIN'T OVER YET!
HEY - - WHAT'S EVERYBODY DOIN'?

HUH? HEY!
HEY!
WHERE'S EVERYBODY GOIN'?

WHAT TH'? WHAT'S GOIN' ON?
HOLY COW!

LOOKS LIKE TH' TABLES HAVE BEEN TURNED, PAL! EXCUSE ME WHILE I GET BACK TO TH' WINNING END OF TH' BAR!

MAN!
WHADDYA DOIN', SMILEY? GIVIN' THIS STUFF AWAY?

GIMME THAT!
GIMME THAT!
HERE! HERE! YOU! GIMME THAT!
EVERYBODY! HAND 'EM OVER!

WHAT, ARE YOU CRAZY?! HOW ARE WE SUPPOSED TO TURN A PROFIT IF YOU GIVE TH' BEER AWAY?!!
I'VE HAD IT WITH THAT RUNT.
ME, TOO.
LUCIUS OR NO LUCIUS, THIS TIME LET'S FIX 'EM FOR GOOD!

GET 'EM!

LOOK OUT!
I WISH FONE BONE'S DRAGON WERE HERE!

WHAT DID YOU SAY?

HOLD IT, BOYS.
DID YOU JUST SAY SOMETHIN' ABOUT A **DRAGON**?

BONK
GO ON, BONE! ANSWER HIM!
YEAH, ANSWER ME!
WHAT DID YOU SAY ABOUT A DRAGON?
GULP!

I - - I - - UH - -
I JUST SAID I WISH
FONE BONE'S DRAGON
WAS HERE . . .

GASP!
GASP!
FONE BONE
HAS A
DRAGON?
GASP!
I DON'T
BELIEVE IT.

WHO'S
FONE BONE?
HE'S THAT
OTHER BONE!
THEIR
COUSIN!

YEAH, RIGHT . . .
TH' ONE WHO'S
ALWAYS HANGIN'
AROUND WITH
THORN!

SO WHERE IS
THIS COUSIN OF
YOURS NOW?
YEAH! AN'
WHERE'S THE
DRAGON?!
ALL RIGHT,
THAT'S ENOUGH!
QUIT
CROWDIN' TH'
BAR!

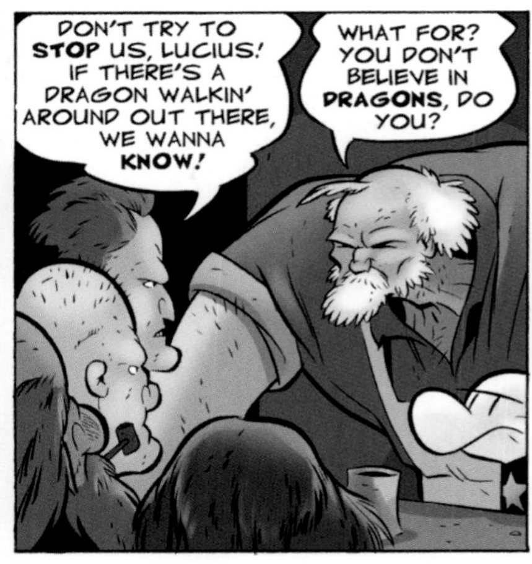
DON'T TRY TO STOP US, LUCIUS! IF THERE'S A DRAGON WALKIN' AROUND OUT THERE, WE WANNA KNOW!
WHAT FOR? YOU DON'T BELIEVE IN DRAGONS, DO YOU?

I DIDN'T SAY I BELIEVED IN 'EM . . . BUT THERE HAVE BEEN SOME PRETTY STRANGE THINGS GOIN' ON HERE LATELY!
STRANGE ENOUGH TO MAKE YOU START BELIEVIN' IN CHILDREN'S STORIES?

I KNOW IT SOUNDS CRAZY, BUT PEOPLE BEEN SEEIN' STRANGE THINGS IN TH' WOODS AT NIGHT! FOLKS ARE AFRAID TO GO OUT!
IT'S TRUE!

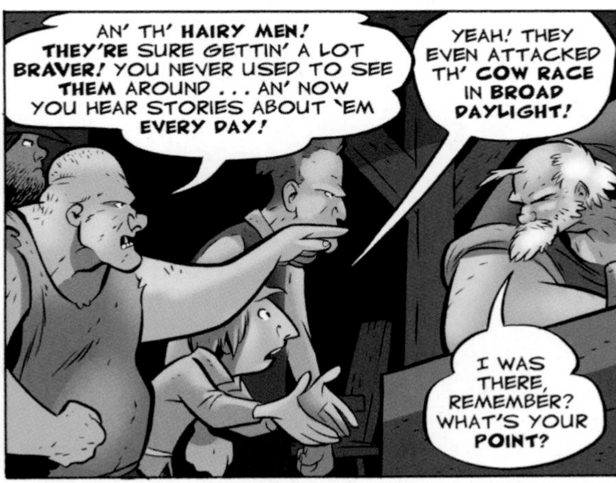
AN' TH' HAIRY MEN! THEY'RE SURE GETTIN' A LOT BRAVER! YOU NEVER USED TO SEE THEM AROUND . . . AN' NOW YOU HEAR STORIES ABOUT 'EM EVERY DAY!
YEAH! THEY EVEN ATTACKED TH' COW RACE IN BROAD DAYLIGHT!
I WAS THERE, REMEMBER? WHAT'S YOUR POINT?

IT ALL STARTED JUST ABOUT TH' SAME TIME THESE TWO SHOWED UP!
EVERYTHING WAS FINE UNTIL TH' BONES CAME TO OUR PART OF TH' VALLEY!

NOW ALL WE GOT IS TROUBLE!
LOOK HERE, BUB, I DON'T KNOW WHOSE DRAGON THIS IS, BUT IT AIN'T OURS! TH' ONLY DRAGON I'VE SEEN IS A BIG, LAZY ORANGE ONE, AN' HE WAS ALREADY HERE!

GASP!
I GOT NEWS FOR YA, GASPING BOY! YOU GOT A LOTTA WEIRD STUFF IN THIS CRAZY VALLEY, SO DON'T GO BLAMIN' US FOR YOUR DRAGON PROBLEMS!

BIG AN' ORANGE! THEN IT'S TRUE!
WHAT'S TRUE? YOU'RE NOT GONNA BELIEVE ANYTHING PHONEY BONE TELLS YOU, ARE YA? YOU CAN'T TRUST THIS RUNT AS FAR AS YOU CAN THROW HIM!

HE'S TELLIN' TH' TRUTH, LUCIUS! WE GOT US A REAL, LIVE DRAGON WALKIN' AROUND OUT THERE!
YOU TAKE TH' CAKE, WENDELL, YOU KNOW THAT?

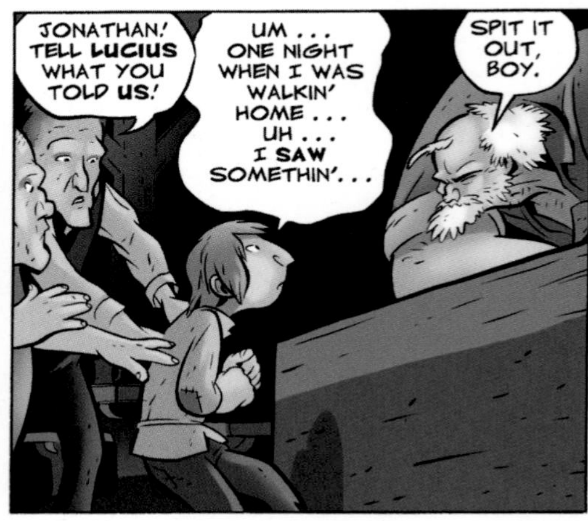
JONATHAN! TELL LUCIUS WHAT YOU TOLD US!
UM . . . ONE NIGHT WHEN I WAS WALKIN' HOME . . . UH . . . I SAW SOMETHIN'. . .
SPIT IT OUT, BOY.

THERE WASN'T HARDLY ANY MOON OUT, SO IT WAS KINDA DARK. AN' REAL QUIET. THEN I SAW IT. A HUGE SHAPE MOVIN' BETWEEN TH' TREES! IT WAS BIG AND IT WAS ORANGE - - AND WHEN IT WAS GONE, ALL THAT WAS LEFT WAS TH' SMELL OF BRIMSTONE!

THERE, SEE? WHAT DO YOU SAY TO THAT, LUCIUS? STILL THINK DRAGONS ARE JUST CHILDREN'S STORIES?
AAH!
I AIN'T GOT NOTHIN' TO SAY. . .

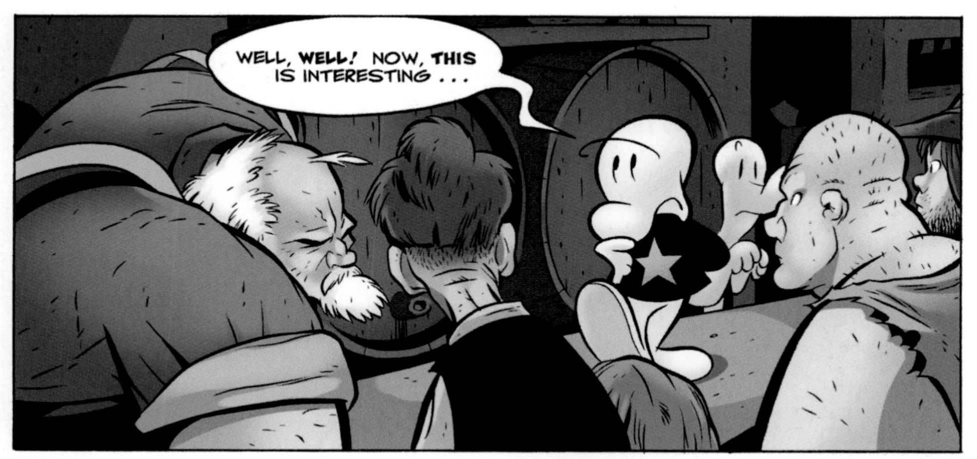
WELL, WELL! NOW, THIS IS INTERESTING . . .

YOU SAY YOU'VE SEEN SHAPES IN TH' WOODS . . . HEARD BUMPS IN TH' NIGHT . . .

. . . YOU SAY IT'S NOT SAFE TO GO OUTSIDE AFTER DARK . . .

YESSIR, I'VE SEEN THESE SYMPTOMS BEFORE!

OH, YOU THINK IT'LL NEVER HAPPEN IN A NICE, QUIET, LITTLE TOWN LIKE THIS . . . BUT YOU CAN'T STOP 'EM! THEY'RE HERE TO STAY!

WHAT ARE YOU **TALKIN'** ABOUT?
WELL, I HATE TO **SAY** THIS, BUT I THINK IT'S SAFE TO **ASSUME** THAT IF YOU HAVE **ONE** DRAGON, THERE'S **BOUND** TO BE **OTHERS!**

OH, MY **GOSH!** THERE'S PROBABLY DRAGONS **EVERYWHERE!**
I **KNEW** IT! THEY'RE TRYIN' TO **TAKE OVER!**

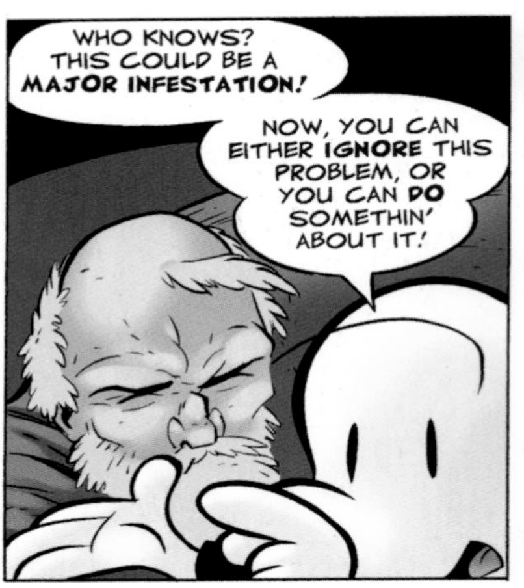
WHO KNOWS? THIS COULD BE A **MAJOR INFESTATION!**
NOW, YOU CAN EITHER **IGNORE** THIS PROBLEM, OR YOU CAN **DO** SOMETHIN' ABOUT IT!

HE'S RIGHT! WE GOTTA **DO** SOMETHIN' BEFORE IT'S TOO **LATE!**
RRR!
IT'S **US** AGAINST **THEM!**
WE'RE NOT GONNA TAKE THIS **SITTIN' DOWN!**

TELL US WHAT WE GOTTA DO!
THE **SAME** THING YOU DO WHEN YOU GOT **ANY** KIND OF PEST CONTROL PROBLEM . . . YOU GET AN **EXTERMINATOR!**
RRR!

AND WHERE DO WE **GET** AN EXTERMINATOR?
GRRR!
RRR!
YER LOOKIN' AT ONE!
PHONCIBLE P. BONE: DRAGONSLAYER!
AT YOUR SERVICE!

WHAT TH' HELL DO YOU THINK YOU'RE DOIN'?
YOU KNOW THIS LITTLE **BET** YOU AN' I GOT GOIN' TO SEE WHO CAN SELL TH' MOST **BEER?**

YEAH?
I'M ABOUT TO WIN!

SMILEY! START POURIN'!
NOTHIN' LIKE A LITTLE ALCOHOL TO GREASE TH' WHEELS OF MOB MENTALITY! RIGHT, BOYS?!

RIGHT!
YAY!
THE FIRST ROUND'S ON **ME!** BUT AFTER **THAT,** YOU GOTTA **PAY!**

THREE CHEERS FOR PHONEY!
THAT'S IT!

THIS HAS GONE FAR ENOUGH! I---

WELCOME, STRANGER. CAN I HELP YOU? YOU NEED A ROOM, OR JUST LOOKIN' TO SLAKE YOUR THIRST?

I BRING NEWS FROM THE SOUTH.
WAIT FOR ME OUTSIDE.

HEY THERE, FONE BONE! HOW YOU DOIN' THESE FINE DAYS?

HELLO, TED! I'M DOIN' OKAY . . . THORN AN' GRAN'MA BEN COULD BE BETTER . . .
HOW ABOUT YOU?
GOOD! JUST BEEN TA SEE LUCIUS AN' YER COUSINS!

OH, YEAH? HOW ARE THEY? ARE THEY CAUSIN' ANY TROUBLE?
THEY'S KICKIN' UP SOME DUST, YOU KNOW, JES LIKE THEY DO. BUT WHAT'S ALL THIS YOU SAYIN' 'BOUTS GRAN'MA AN' THORNY? SOMETHIN' WRONG?

WELL, THORN IS OUT IN TH' BARN LAYIN' FACEDOWN IN TH' HAY. SHE'S PRETTY UPSET. SHE GOT SOME BAD NEWS ABOUT HER PARENTS, AN' SOME OTHER STUFF ABOUT HER PAST . . .
LIKE WHAT?

OH, UH, I PROBABLY SHOULDN'T SAY, TED. I MEAN, I TRUST YOU, BUT I THINK THEY'RE KINDA SECRET - -
SHE FIND OUT HER FOLKS WAS KILLED BY RAT CREATURES?

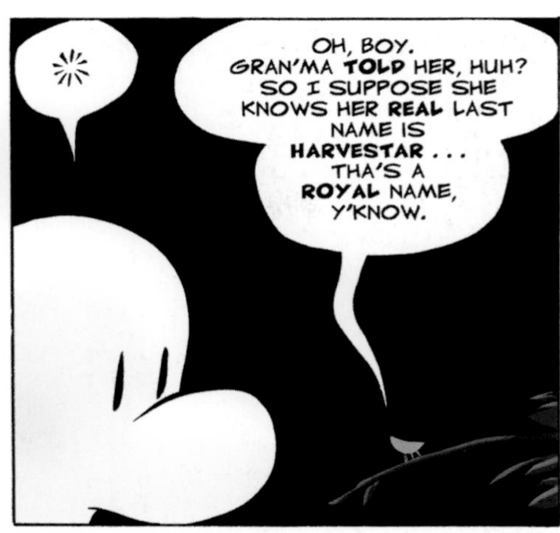
OH, BOY. GRAN'MA TOLD HER, HUH? SO I SUPPOSE SHE KNOWS HER REAL LAST NAME IS HARVESTAR . . . THA'S A ROYAL NAME, Y'KNOW.

UM, YEAH. SHE KNOWS. GRAN'MA TOLD HER.
THORN HARVESTAR. CROWN PRINCESS OF TH' WHOLE SHOOTIN' MATCH! BIG STUFF, BIG STUFF.

HOW DID YOU KNOW THAT? THORN DIDN'T EVEN KNOW!
BUGS KNOW A LOTTA STUFF FOLKS WOULDN'T S'POSE THEY'D KNOW.
SAY, THAT REMINDS ME, I GOT AN IMPORTANT MESSAGE FROM LUCIUS FOR GRAN'MA BEN! WHERE IS SHE?

SHE WAS IN TH' HOUSE LAST I SAW HER.
OKEE DOKEE, BONE! CATCH YA LATER, BYE!

BYE!

SLAM!

HEY, BONE! GO GRAB YOUR KNAPSACK AN' MEET ME IN TH' BARN! **NOW!**

YES, MA'AM!

SHUNK

GET UP, THORN.
I JUST RECEIVED WORD THAT TH' SITUATION DOWN SOUTH HAS **CHANGED . . .**

GRAN'MA - - ?
WE HAVE TO LEAVE.

HERE'S YOUR BEDROLL AND A FEW OF YOUR PERSONAL THINGS . . .

C'MON IN HERE, BONE.
ACCORDING TO MY SOURCES, SOMEONE IS GATHERING AN ARMY IN THE EASTERN MOUNTAINS AND THAT PERSON IS WEARING A HOOD.

IF IT'S THE SAME HOODED FIGURE FROM THORN'S DREAMS, THEN THE RAT CREATURES KNOW WHO WE ARE.
THERE'S MORE BAD NEWS . . .

IT SEEMS LARGE NUMBERS OF RAT CREATURES ARE HEADING THIS WAY.

HERE? THEY'RE COMING HERE? WHY?
THEY'RE NOT OUT ON A PICNIC, BONE! IT'S NOT SAFE HERE ANYMORE. WE HAVE TO LEAVE NOW. ANYTHING IN TH' HOUSE YOU NEED BEFORE WE GET STARTED?

I -- MIGHT NEED SOMETHING WARMER TO WEAR . . .

I'LL GRAB YOUR CLOAK WHEN I GO BACK IN FOR TH' FOOD. AND WHILE I'M DOIN' THAT I WANT YOU TO CLEAR AWAY ALL THIS STRAW.

THERE'S A SECRET DOOR UNDER THERE, AN' INSIDE IS AN OLD TRUNK. HAUL IT OUTTA THERE AN' I'LL BE RIGHT BACK!

YOU GOT IT? GOOD!

OKAY, STEP BACK.

HAND ME YOUR **KNAPSACK**, BONE.

HERE.
TAKE GOOD CARE OF THIS NOW.

BETTER COVER THIS UP WITH SOMETHIN'.

WHAT ARE YOU LOOKIN' AT? I USED TO WEAR THIS THING ALL TH' TIME!

ALL RIGHT, LOAD UP! AN' MAKE SURE YOUR PACKS ARE TIED DOWN GOOD AN' TIGHT! WE GOT A LONG WALK AHEAD OF US!

THAT'S IT? WE'RE JUST GONNA LEAVE?!
THAT'S IT.

YOU'VE BEEN AWFUL QUIET, THORN. YOU GONNA BE OKAY?
I'M FINE IF YOU ARE.

THEN LET'S GO.

TO BE CONTINUED...

About Jeff Smith

Jeff Smith was born and raised in the American Midwest. He learned about cartooning from comic strips, comic books, and watching animated shorts on TV. After four years of drawing comic strips for Ohio State University's student newspaper and co-founding Character Builders animation studio in 1986, Smith launched the comic book *BONE* in 1991. Between *BONE* and other comics projects Smith spends much of his time on the international guest circuit promoting comics and the art of graphic novels.

More About *BONE*

Instant classics when they first appeared as underground comic books in 1991, the *BONE* books have since garnered 38 international awards and sold a million copies in 15 languages. Now HarperCollins is publishing, for the first time in the UK, full-colour graphic novel editions of the series. Look out for the continuing adventures of the Bone cousins in the fourth book, *The Dragon Slayer*.

WATERFALL
DRAGON'S STAIR
DEREN GARD
HOT SPRINGS
OLD MAN'S CAVE
GRAN'MA BEN'S FARM
BARRELHAVEN TAVERN
THE FAIRGROUNDS
KNOTT'S DEFEAT
N
E
W
S
STONY
The Valley

EASTERN MOUNTAINS
RAT CREATURE TEMPLE
CONKLE'S HOLLOW
UPPER PAWA
PAWA
PRAYER STONE HILL
TANEN GARD
FLINT RIDGE
THE GREAT BASIN
PAWA ROAD
ATHEIA
GULCH
SINNER'S ROCK
MC

The BONE series:

Out from Boneville
The Great Cow Race